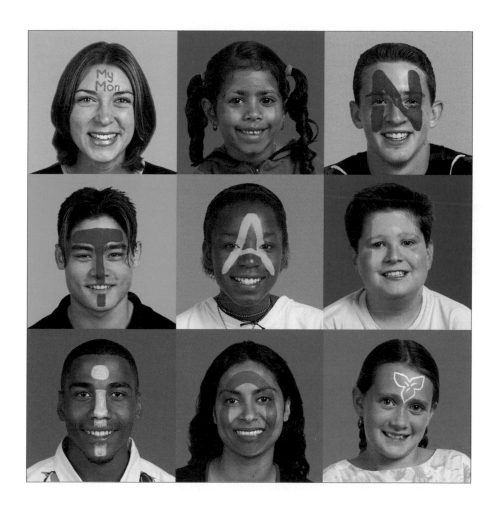

SHAPING THE FUTURE TOGETHER

FAÇONNONS ENSEMBLE NOTRE AVENIR

ONTARIO

2

**The Premier
of Ontario**

Legislative Building
Queen's Park
Toronto, Ontario
M7A 1A1

**Le Premier ministre
de l'Ontario**

Hôtel du gouvernement
Queen's Park
Toronto (Ontario)
M7A 1A1

Ontario

Message from the Premier of Ontario

Of the many projects set up across our province to celebrate the new millennium, none exceeds *My Ontario* for reaching out to young people.

In words and in pictures, tens of thousands of young Ontarians responded to our invitation to share their hopes and plans for the future.

These pages show their imagination, their humour and their wisdom. They reveal our young people's faith in humanity and in themselves. Page after page shows their vision of the future and how they hope to turn their dreams into reality.

As Ontarians, we are all proud of the individuality and creativity that is a hallmark of our province and our country. *My Ontario* captures this remarkable strength — a strength that will ensure our province's growth.

I believe the future of our province is limited only by the talents, aspirations and determination of our people. Through their contributions to this project, our young people have shown that as we enter a new millennium, this future is without bounds.

Congratulations to all who contributed to *My Ontario*. It is a collection that will add significantly to our millennium celebrations.

Sincerely,

Michael D. Harris, MPP

 Ontario

The Premier
of Ontario

Le Premier ministre
de l'Ontario

Ontario

3

Legislative Building
Queen's Park
Toronto, Ontario
M7A 1A1

Hôtel du gouvernement
Queen's Park
Toronto (Ontario)
M7A 1A1

Un message du Premier ministre de l'Ontario

Parmi les nombreux projets qui sont montés à travers notre province dans le but de fêter l'avènement du nouveau millénaire, nul ne rejoint nos jeunes comme *Mon Ontario*.

En mots et en images, des dizaines de milliers de jeunes Ontariens et Ontariennes ont répondu à notre invitation d'exprimer leurs espoirs et leurs projets quant à l'avenir.

Les pages suivantes montrent l'imagination, le sens de l'humour et la sagesse de nos jeunes. Elles révèlent la foi qu'ils ont en l'humanité et en eux-mêmes. Page après page, ils nous exposent leur vision de l'avenir et les façons dont ils espèrent faire de leurs rêves des réalités.

En tant qu'Ontariens et Ontariennes, nous sommes tous fiers de l'individualité et de la créativité qui sont des marques de notre province et de notre pays. *Mon Ontario* canalise cette force remarquable, une force qui permettra d'assurer la croissance de notre province.

Je crois que l'avenir de notre province ne sera limité que par les talents, les aspirations et la détermination de nos gens. Grâce à leurs contributions à ce projet, nos jeunes ont démontré qu'à l'amorce d'un nouveau millénaire, cet avenir est sans borne.

Je félicite toutes les personnes qui ont contribué à *Mon Ontario*. Cette collection ajoutera grandement à nos fêtes du nouveau millénaire.

Veuillez agréer l'expression de mes sentiments les meilleurs.

Le député provincial,

Michael D. Harris

4

Ministry of Citizenship,
Culture and Recreation

Minister

6th Floor
400 University Avenue
Toronto ON M7A 2R9
Tel.: (416) 325-6200
Fax: (416) 325-6195

Ministére des Affaires civiques,
de la Culture et des Loisirs

Ministre

6ᵉ étage
400, avenue University
Toronto ON M7A 2R9
Tél. : (416) 325-6200
Téléc. : (416) 325-6195

Ontario

Message from Helen Johns,
Minister of Citizenship, Culture and Recreation

When the provincial government began planning Ontario 2000, its commemorative project to celebrate the new millennium, we agreed — right from the start — that we should focus on Ontario's young people.

Through their dreams and talents, our girls and boys, young men and young women will be building Ontario's future.

Through the *My Ontario* project, we asked students across the province to share their imagination with us — to think about what the world of tomorrow ought to be for themselves and their families. With the cooperation of school boards, teachers and parents, we had tens of thousands of Ontario students from junior kindergarten to OAC responding to our invitation.

This flood of wild, creative, amazing ideas of what the province will be like in the year 2020 has inspired everyone working with the project. We have a wonderful world ahead!

A central review team had the challenging job of choosing submissions that reflect Ontario's many vibrant communities. You'll find the result of that work in *My Ontario,* which is now in every school and library in the province.

Memento is a personal version of *My Ontario* that we're proud to share with each of the province's more than two million elementary and high school students. It includes selections from the library edition along with pages where each student can record his or her creative ideas.

I hope you'll read *My Ontario* with delight, surprise and a great deal of hope for the future. You can already see our province will be in good hands.

Helen Johns
Minister

Ministry of Citizenship,
Culture and Recreation

Minister

6th Floor
400 University Avenue
Toronto ON M7A 2R9
Tel.: (416) 325-6200
Fax: (416) 325-6195

Ministére des Affaires civiques,
de la Culture et des Loisirs

Ministre

6ᵉ étage
400, avenue University
Toronto ON M7A 2R9
Tél. : (416) 325-6200
Téléc. : (416) 325-6195

Ontario

Message d'Helen Johns,
ministre des Affaires civiques, de la Culture et des Loisirs

ONTARIO

Lorsque le gouvernement provincial a commencé à planifier Ontario 2000, son projet commémoratif visant à célébrer le nouveau millénaire, nous avions décidé, dès le départ, de mettre l'accent sur les jeunes de l'Ontario.

Ce sont les rêves et les talents des jeunes filles et garçons et des jeunes gens qui permettront de bâtir l'avenir de la province.

Dans le cadre du projet *Mon Ontario*, nous avons demandé aux élèves de toute la province de faire preuve d'imagination et de nous décrire leur vision du monde de demain, tant pour eux que pour leur famille. Grâce à la collaboration des conseils scolaires, du personnel enseignant et des parents, des centaines de milliers d'élèves de la province, de la maternelle aux CPO, ont répondu à notre invitation.

Ces descriptions originales, créatives et étonnantes de ce que la province sera en l'an 2020 ont inspiré toutes les personnes qui œuvrent au projet. Un monde merveilleux nous attend!

On a confié à une équipe d'étude centrale la tâche passionnante de choisir les soumissions qui reflètent le dynamisme des nombreuses collectivités ontariennes. Vous pourrez admirer le fruit de ces travaux dans *Mon Ontario*, ouvrage qui se trouve maintenant dans chaque école et bibliothèque de la province.

Mémento est une version personnalisée de *Mon Ontario* que nous avons le plaisir de partager avec les plus de deux millions d'élèves des écoles élémentaires et secondaires de la province. Il inclut des extraits de l'édition de bibliothèque de même que des pages sur lesquelles chaque élève peut consigner ses idées créatives.

J'espère que vous trouverez la lecture de *Mon Ontario* agréable, surprenante et source d'espoir pour l'avenir. Vous pouvez constater que la province sera entre de bonnes mains.

L'honorable Helen Johns
Ministre

6

My Diary

Dear Diary,

Today in school, my teacher announced that we (like many other schools in Ontario) would be participating in the "My Ontario" project (the one advertised on the radio). He explained that the task would involve sharing our individual beliefs, dreams and predictions of what the year will be like in our province. Personally, I will be in my mid-thirties, so it made me start asking and wondering to myself: what new technology and advancements will be introduced, where will my personal life be (raising a family, children, marriage...), and what things will I have done to help others?

This project is interesting and unique because it takes thousands of different students of all ages in Ontario and compiles their aspirations. When they publish this book of stories and predictions, I will take time to read it. I like seeing what others my own age are hoping to do in the coming years because, after all, they say "the children of the present are tomorrow's future."

I've decided to share my feelings of what I will strive for in 2020 in you, my diary, so that when I am older and this year eventually does come, I shall be able to reflect and look back to see if I was at all close.

There are numerous things that I wish to accomplish before, and also during, 2020. I will separate my thoughts into different categories, each relating to their own subject (i.e., family, occupations, what Ontario will be like, etc.).

First of all, family. By the time I am 30, I hope to have been married for a few years, around three or four (having completed all the schooling necessary for the occupation that I wish to have). I hope for some children also, an average size family of 4 or 5 (including kids and adults) for me and my husband to care for. The reason I would love to have a larger family is because I get along well with children and I would love my kids very much.

Families in 2020 will, if compared, be similar to the average-style family today. Only the materialistic things around us will be altered over and over again. Things like society, government and money can, and most certainly will, change, becoming more and more advanced and structured day by day, year by year.

One of my goals is to be a teacher when I grow up. I have thought about this for a few years, since I was in grade 5. Helping people to learn new things must be a wonderful experience, letting them achieve whatever they care for. That is the impact that I would like to leave people with (even if it is small), helping someone to learn and taking interest in what they are saying. Others in my class do not have the same taste in jobs that I do but that is fine. There are numerous ways you can help people — in the fields of medicine, science, politics, and many more occupations. Everyone has his or her own way of expressing their talents and gifts whether it has a title or not. In the long run, all can benefit if you do your best and live to your true potential.

As far as education, jobs, and business in our world go, it is easy to predict that by 2020 they will be extremely high-tech. So, yes, although many things will change and many will not, Ontario is going to keep up with all the latest trends, events, and huge media newscasts.

Those are my thoughts on what I perceive will happen in 2020. I am dating this entry in you, diary, so that I will always have a record of what my opinions about Ontario in 2020 were at 13 years of age in 1999.

April 1999

Jamie Danielle Nikolaou
Bruce-Grey Catholic District School Board
Grade 8

7

People
Les gens

8

Ready or Not, Here It Comes:
The following is the prediction of what the world will be like in the year 2020.

Many hopes and dreams will come true for our young society of today in the year 2020. Those who dreamed of being doctors may be doctors and those who dreamed and worked hard to be scientists may be scientists, but one thing can be said about the year 2020, "nothing will be the same!" The world as it is known will have evolved into a new civilization where promises that are made are kept. If there were something that the world can do to help improve the future now, it would be to start keeping promises. The new generation will be the leaders of the world, and the weight of the future lies in the education that they receive today.

It is only 21 years from now, but much can happen in those 21 years. It is hoped that the future will be full of life and happiness, instead of what it is today with dull moods and dark colors. Life almost seems to drag on these days, and there is no climax, which we are all striving for in the end of the chapter. The year 2020 holds many possibilities, but those possibilities depend on the actions we make today. It would be nice to see cleaner transportation as well, or else there will be no year 2020.

We can all work on improving little things, such as the way we treat others, or the way we waste food and litter a little here and there. All of these tiny things will alter the existence of new things to come, and if the present does not work on it, then there will be no future to fix the mistakes and keep on learning and educating others.

Family life styles will be as they are in the present in the year 2020, and so will the lives that they lead. The jobs and sacrifices that the parents have to make will all be vanquished, and they will live lives without the ball and chain around their ankles, which is attached at the other end to a desk. The society of today can also learn to speak freely a little more. The louder they speak the more that will get done, such as in the classrooms. In the year 2020 everyone should have their own opinion, not that they do not have one today, it's just everyone will not follow the leader, they will all strive their own way, and pick their own path.

In the year 2020 it can be hoped that there will be no let downs or disappointment, because this is a number one stress causer and the future in the minds of the youth should have no stress. The present needs to work on releasing emotions and feelings and become open minded to new things, especially in the school atmosphere. The grownups of today have a few things to work on here and there, like allowing the kids to express themselves and not have to follow what they think is right, but the kids also have to be willing to listen and learn and obey the rules. If all goes well and the present works on the few things mentioned then the world in the year 2020 should be a livable place, as long as we all work together. Remember, the future can't *happen* if we are not ready for it, it's coming ready or not, so why not listen to each other and be ready.

Laura Vandervoort

Grade 9 / 9e année
Toronto District School Board

Diversity

In the year 2020, despite the technological advancements, I believe people will remain the most valuable resource. It will be ever so important to recognize the strength of diversity. We need to acknowledge and develop healthy relationships between people of different religions, races, and cultures, and respect everyone's point of view.

Grade 9 / 9e année
Toronto District School Board

Hilary Brown

2020 Fashion

10

By year 2020
This is the fashion.

Krystal Chung

Grade 3 / 3e année
Toronto District School Board

My Dreams

In the year 2020 what do you think Ontario will be like? Will it be a disaster or will it be better than now? Lots of people have dreams and I, Katie Komisar, want to tell you what my dreams are. I hope that the poor people on the street will at least get a home by the year 2020, because junkyards and old broken houses which don't have warmth or anything are not good enough for people just like us.

Here is another important dream to me. I wish that cars would be more safe when people get into accidents. Lots of cars have airbags but they aren't always enough to save our lives if you get into a big accident. So why don't they make a car or any type of vehicle with more protection and safety features?

Now this is my last but not least dream. You know all those commercials that show children and families with flies on them and they are sooooooo skinny that they can hardly breathe? I wish they could get a good home and enough food to take care of their families!!!

P.S. In the year 2020 if any bosses need gymnastic coaches I will surely try to volunteer. Please make my dreams come true.

Grade 4 / 4ᵉ année   **Katie Komisar**

12

My Ontario: Over the Rainbow

Janice opened her eyes as a loud, thundering sound bolted into her ears. I'm in Ontario, she remembered. A wave of excitement went down her spine. She had been sent away from her country, Jordan, for there was too much violence there.

She slowly got off the airplane.

Soon she got in a taxi and headed off to her Aunt Josphene's farm. As she looked out the window, her eyes filled up with joy. The place, this Ontario, was so perfect.

She had heard of the great CN Tower and the SkyDome. She had also heard of the luxurious land and wide space in the countryside.

Her eyes filled with excitement as she headed toward the city. So many people, so many stores. She watched as a mother and her two sons walked down the street, laughing and talking. Janice could see the love in their eyes.

As the taxi approached the lake, Janice saw many people doing different things. There were people water skiing, surfing, and playing beach volleyball. She waved to everyone there. Surprisingly, they waved back!

Soon the taxi came to her aunt's farm. Janice ran out and hugged her aunt. She was right. This was the land over the rainbow.

Ashima Bhatt

Grade 7 / 7ᵉ année
Durham District School Board

Jesse the Mom

"When I'm grown up, in the year 2020, I would like to be

by: Jesse

Grade SK / Jardin
York Region District School Board

Jesselyn Cook

14

Lending a Helping Hand

Ontario In 2020

In the year 2020 I would like to see rich giving money to the poor, and I would have lots of shelters for the poor. People would give food to the people in need. People wouldn't litter the environment and I would pick up the garbage. But I think every adult should have a job. People shouldn't pollute Ontario, and they should plant lots of trees so it would stop the polluting. Every person would have a house and no one would be poor. This is my year 2020. The end.

Grade 2 / 2e année
Catholic District School Board
of Eastern Ontario

James Elmhirst

16

The Future of Ontario Class Project

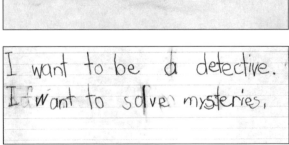

I want to be a detective. I want to solve mysteries.

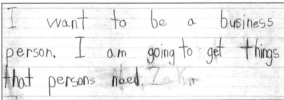

I want to be a business person. I am going to get things that persons need. Zakir

Kenneth

Zakir Hussain Ali

Grade 1 / 1re année

The Future of Ontario Class Project

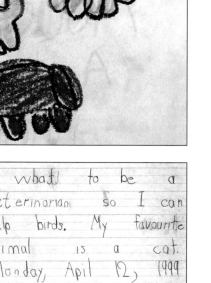

I what to be a
Veterinarian so I can
help birds. My favourite
animal is a cat.
Monday, Apil 12, 1999

I want to be a teacher.
I like helping people and
I like to teaching people
reading. and math.

Stephanie Thibault

Di Huyen

Grade 1 / 1ʳᵉ année

18

The Future of Ontario Class Project

I want to be aon banker. I am goingin to give people money. RehanaRasul

I want to be a builder. I Lu want to build houses. I like to build stuf.

Rehana

Lauren

Grade 1 / 1re année

The Future of Ontario Class Project

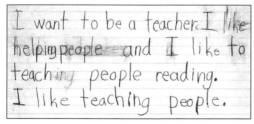

I want to be a teacher. I like
helpimg people and I like to
teaching people reading.
I like teaching people.

Chau Le

I want to be a police officer.
I am going toppat the robr in
gail and tac ther money.

Dante

Grade 1 / 1re année

The Future of Ontario Class Project

20

I want to be a nurse so I can help sick People.

Dannette

I Want to be fire fighter to Put out big.

Kody

Grade 1 / 1re année

The Future of Ontario Class Project

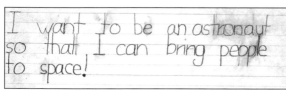

I want to be an astronaut
so that I can bring people
to space!

I want to be a farmr
I wantt take care of animals.

Daniel   Anika

Grade 1 / 1re année

22

The Future of Ontario Class Project

I want to be a actor.
I want to make movies.

I want to be a teacher
and help people.
I want to teach children
to write.

Luke

Klaudia

Grade 1 / 1re année

The Future of Ontario Class Project

23

Lewisha

Grade 1 / 1ʳᵉ année

I want to be a doctor
so I could help kids that is not
well. I want to help old people.

24

Simple Deeds

Take the round living earth
including the people and homes
minus the big factories
and the colour in the sky they tone.

Plant more maple and pine trees
replace the garbage on the ground
clean up the parks in your neighbourhood
pick up a dog from the pound.

Stay in school and get your diploma
attend some courses in college
work your hardest, do your best
don't underestimate your knowledge.

Care for all of those in need
donate your old clothes
give as much as you want to get
always be on your toes.

Find a career you'd love to do
and make it a goal to get there
if everyone had a useful job
wouldn't your life seem fair?

Ontario has so much potential
if we give it what it needs
it doesn't take a lot of effort
just do these simple deeds.

Take a moment to absorb what you feel
to open your eyes and see
time is almost running out
what's your future going to be?

Allison Vader　　　　Grade 8 / 8e année
　　　　　　　　　　　Halton District School Board

Mon ami le parapluie

En 2020, je serai fermière. Afin de me protéger contre les rayons puissants du soleil, je serai obligée de porter avec moi un parapluie quand je travaille.

Maternelle / Grade K
Conseil scolaire du district
des écoles catholiques du Sud-Ouest
de l'Ontario

Amanda Ruggaber

When I Grow Up in 2020

Mitchell Price

Grade SK / Jardin
York Region District School Board

Looking Ahead

Better, worse, or same?
Looking ahead…
How much will change over tewnty-one years? Not for me personally, but worldwide, nationally, provincially. Will things change for better or worse? Who's to say? Maybe things won't change at all…

Which one will it be?

Don't you see it coming?
Looking back…
Tuesday, March 30, 2020
It's hard to believe twenty-one years ago parents even considered letting their children bike to the store, walk around alone in a mall, or even advertise their address in the pen pal section of a magazine. Now we all use the Internet for most things, from our social life (friends in person are becoming very rare), to running the laundry machine (which, unfortunately, has not improved much).

Divorce rates are still rising. Out of a random fifty married people that I talk to on the net, about forty have been divorced at least once.

It's too bad I hadn't gotten into the sunscreen industry. They had to make a new law that forces everyone to buy 400 ml of sunscreen UV 60 for each person in the family every month, since the ozone layer is so thin.

Is it too late to change things? I wish we had taken charge, planned ahead, been creative, motivated ourselves – whatever it would have taken to progress. I often wonder where we would be now…

Take charge of our future.
Looking back…
Tuesday, March 30, 2020
Isn't it amazing how much we can advance in twenty-one years when we get motivated?! Just small steps have helped us in so many ways.

As far as technology is concerned, pretty much everything has been improved more than I could have even imagined in 1999.

Society is far improved. There are so many laws now that protect the environment that the ozone layer is starting to recover.

They hired more fire(wo)men, police(wo)men, crossing guards, geriatric caregivers, doctors and nurses, and built more hospitals, convalescent homes, police and fire stations. Most towns, universities and schools have installed emergency telephones, and provide free counselling.

People's attitude towards life in general has been getting better and better. When we finally realized that things weren't going to get better by themselves, we put our minds to it, got to work, and made a difference.

Grade 8 / 8ᵉ année
Limestone District School Board

Lauren Remmler

**Jason's Millennium
Sonata for Kids**

28

29

30

Fashion in the Year 2020

In the year 2020 the world is going to be a totally different place with a very different style! I think that their clothes are going to have things on them that everybody wants on their clothes today. I think that people will make an outfit that you can plug in a wall, and it will warm you up when you are cold, just like an electric blanket. Maybe they will invent a pair of pants for kids only with every multiplication, division, subtraction and addition that you could think of on it. Maybe people will wear pants with such big pockets that you could fit a minicomputer into one pocket and a CD player into the other pocket.

Clothing designers might even have a shirt that has the entire atlas on it for people who study geography. I think that they could make a shirt made from feathers! Scientists can maybe make a shirt with a time travel machine on it. That would be the best!

Now for the sunny weather. Everybody knows that you need a hat when it's hot. I think that people might wear hats with drinks hanging off them so when it's hot you can pull a drink off and drink away! They might even have a hat where you can push a button and music will play for you. I also think that people will have a hat to wear when they are upset and it will make them happy again. People might even have a hat with a built-in television, so when you get bored you can just take off your hat and watch your favourite cartoons.

These clothes might sound weird to you now, but in the future, you never know, these clothes might one day be the most popular clothes in the world!

Marcus

Grade 5 / 5ᵉ année
Ottawa-Carleton District School Board

What Am I Going to Be in the Year 2020?

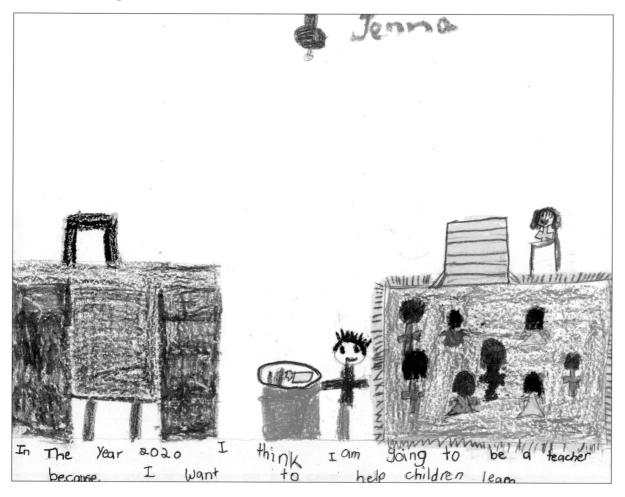

In The Year 2020 I think I am going to be a teacher because I want to help children learn

A Teacher.

Grade 2 / 2e année
Dufferin-Peel Catholic
District School Board

Jenna Furgiuele

32

Ontario is My Home

Make my Ontario peaceful and safe
Yesterday is gone, the future is here
Over the years many things have changed
Never thought this day would finally come
The children are grown, starting lives of their own
All of my people living healthy and strong
Racial conflicts no longer exist
Imperfections and flaws are not judged here
Ontario is my home, the best place to be

Rebecca Lynn Sturgeon Grade 10 / 10e année
Thames Valley District School Board

In the Year 2020...

I think in the year 2020 everyone will have houses to live in and good food to eat. Everyone will be able to read and write and have good behaviour. We will have healthy rivers and everyone will stop doing drugs. I plan to be a teacher helping everyone to learn good behaviour. I will insist there is no junk in the rivers and tell people that drugs are no good.

Kassie Ames Grade 3 / 3e année

Building Houses

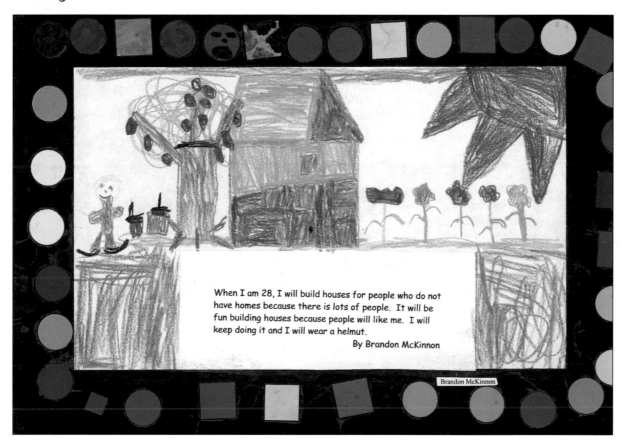

When I am 28, I will build houses for people who do not have homes because there is lots of people. It will be fun building houses because people will like me. I will keep doing it and I will wear a helmut.

By Brandon McKinnon

Brandon McKinnon

Grade 1 / 1re année
Hastings and Prince Edward
District School Board

Brandon McKinnon

34

My Year 2000 Project

When I grow up everything will be different. Twenty years from now I will be 26 years old. I hope all my wishes and dreams come true. I see myself as a teacher, artist, and musician. I will be famous and popular. All the people will come to listen and see how I paint. All the kids will come to me for me to teach them in class. My family will move into a nice house. I want my house to have a pool. I want my puppy to stay little. I want my puppy to have a black eye. The rest of him will be white. I want it to be a boy. I will live in Ontario, the best province in Canada. My home will be in Toronto the best city I've always liked. I will travel to the stars to spend my vacation there. I will keep my baby toys on my table there. Sometimes I will play with my baby toys. I think people will be able to fly in special flying machines. I will put that machine in my right hand and push the red button and fly up to see some cool places. I can't wait till I grow up.

Mia Mǔsić

Grade 1 / 1ʳᵉ année
Toronto District School Board

In the Year 2020 I Believe . . .

In the year 2020 I believe we can have a cleaner environment. In the year 2020 I believe that there will be no harm to animals. In the year 2020 I believe that poverty will be the least of our worries. In the year 2020 I believe that technology will soar with no limits. In the year 2020 I believe that all horrible diseases will be sent out the door of death. In the year 2020 I believe that we can all hold hands together and say "we are one" and to say it doesn't matter what the colour of our skin, our religion, or even our language is, and that we all created this Earth as one. In the year 2020 I believe that there will not be any wars and that innocent lives will not be shattered in the face of hatred.

Grade 6 / 6ᵉ année
Toronto District School Board

Sinthujha Kumarasamy

Fashion Spring 2020

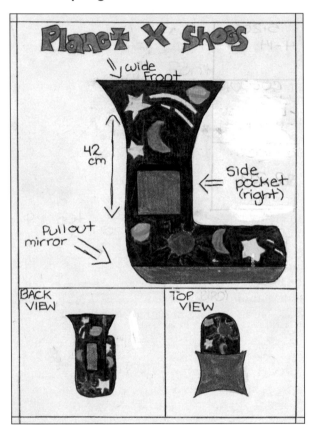

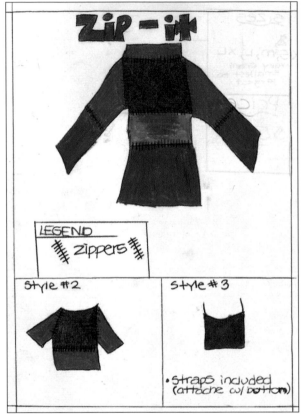

Ashley Scott
Marnie Sheppard

Grade 8 / 8e année
Peel District School Board

My Hopes and Dreams for 2020

My vision for Ontario in the year 2020 is that cures for the deadly diseases like AIDS, cancer and brain tumours will be found. I also believe that the people of the world will try to fulfill God's idea of peace on earth. I hope that we will also make attempts to not pollute the world by lessening the production of items that we do not need.

I believe that cancer is probably the most deadly disease and I am sure that cancer can be beaten. To decrease the population of Ontario from getting a disease like lung cancer there should be a law against stores and gas stations selling cigarettes. I also believe that a group of scientists will get together and find a cure for any other cancers, brain tumours, and maybe even AIDS. I could contribute to this cause by donating money to give scientists more research time.

I hope that people of our world will learn how to be kind to each other and keep peace in our world. You don't have to do anything major like stopping a war or something. You could just do something little like trying to keep peace in your own house. At least you're attempting to keep peace. If you wanted to try and keep peace somewhere other than at home, try keeping peace at school. You could become a peer mediator and stop kids from having fights in the schoolyard. I will contribute to this by keeping peace in my own home by not fighting with my brother and maybe I will even become a peer mediator. I hope

everyone will at least attempt to keep peace and try not to start fights for silly reasons.

We, as people of our world, should not only try and keep peace in our world but we should also try not polluting our world. To not pollute the world you could stop throwing your candy wrappers and your plastic drink containers out your car windows. You could also ride your bike or walk to a friend's house, if they live close, instead of getting your parents to drive you. You could also ask your parents to stop buying things in the grocery stores that are covered in plastic wrappings. Every time you get a bit of money from your grandparents or from your allowance, before you go out and buy that toy you want, think twice about it. It could be an item that comes from a huge factory and the huge factory is one of the reasons why the earth is so polluted. So think about it before you buy it.

So, what I am hoping for in the year 2020 is cures for the deadly diseases, peace on earth, and that earth will not be as polluted as it is now. We can all do our part in making these dreams come true. Even if it is as little as picking up a few pieces of garbage, keeping peace in your own home, or sending money to give scientists more research time, at least you have made attempts and contributed to God's idea of a healthy and happy environment

Grade 7 / 7ᵉ année
Dufferin-Peel Catholic District School Board

Sarah Cramp

Growing Up in the New Millennium

When I'm grown up, in the year 2020, I would like to be an artist.

by: Taryn

Taryn Deasley

Grade SK / Jardin
York Region District School Board

Peace in Plenty

In the year 2020
Might we all say:
We'll have peace in plenty…
Man, we'd like it that way

How will we achieve peace anyway?
Communication, talking together
But that's just one way
And to flock like birds of a feather

We will find a way to say things with love
And to do our very best
Just like the peace symbol and the dove
No matter how big the test

And of course in the year 2020
There will be peace in plenty

Grade 5 / 5e année   **Amanda Richardson**
Cristina Rizzo

When I'm 25

40

Ryan Reid

Grade K / Maternelle
Hastings and Prince Edward
District School Board

41

Attitudes Are the Real Disability

At 10 years old, as I sit here in my wheelchair gazing beyond the horizon to the year 2020, my vision and belief is for an Ontario free of barriers, attitudes, and for more common grounds.

I search for the freedom, to go anywhere in my beautiful province and access the parks, family and friends' homes, buildings, schools, going on trains, planes, without any difficulty at all.

Although the year 2020 seems so far away, it really isn't when I think of the biggest challenge I want to change and that is, "attitudes" towards people with disabilities. "ATTITUDES" ARE THE REAL DISABILITY.

With a barrier free Ontario, and people accepted for who they are, and what they can accomplish, that will naturally bring us all to a more common ground. For I believe that we all have equal rights.

When the year 2020 arrives I will sit gazing out, not beyond a horizon but out into a classroom of students. This is another vision I have, that I feel will make a difference in the province of Ontario. To be a teacher that this province will be proud of.

I believe I can make my vision a reality by the year 2020 and contribute to the future of My Ontario. I am committed to dedicating my time and knowledge and personal experience by educating my community, the schools including students and teachers, government, builders, and many others on awareness about disabilities, the need for a barrier free environment, an equal opportunity for all people in Ontario.

Grade 5 / 5ᵉ année
Toronto District School Board

Sarah L. Dell

42

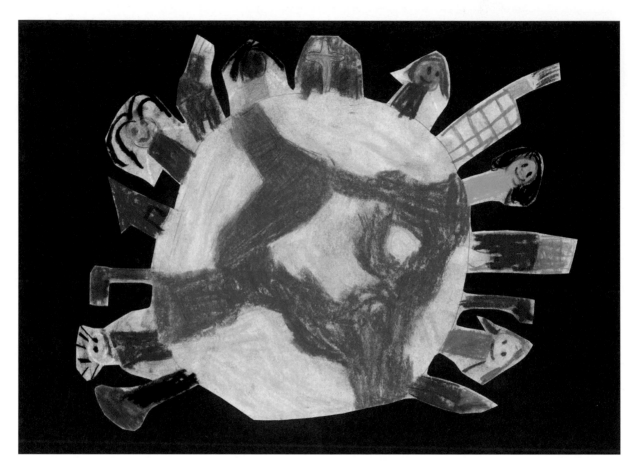

Our Earth

My picture is about a world where people are nice.

Dao Bui
Grade 3 / 3e année
Toronto District School Board

Arts & Culture

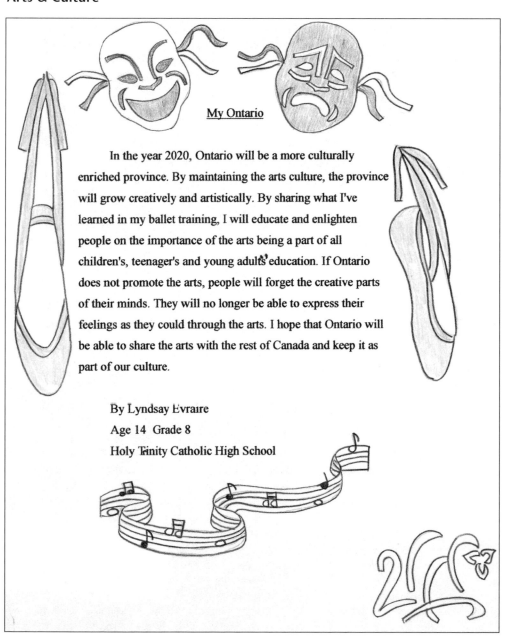

My Ontario

In the year 2020, Ontario will be a more culturally enriched province. By maintaining the arts culture, the province will grow creatively and artistically. By sharing what I've learned in my ballet training, I will educate and enlighten people on the importance of the arts being a part of all children's, teenager's and young adults' education. If Ontario does not promote the arts, people will forget the creative parts of their minds. They will no longer be able to express their feelings as they could through the arts. I hope that Ontario will be able to share the arts with the rest of Canada and keep it as part of our culture.

By Lyndsay Evraire
Age 14 Grade 8
Holy Trinity Catholic High School

44

I Had a Dream

"Ladies and gentlemen, I would like to present to you the president and founder of this wonderful organization, F.R.E.E.D.O.M., and the man of the hour, please welcome Dr. Alexander Spinelli."

Thank you, Bob, as all of you know, we started this organization 40 years ago. In these past 40 years we have accomplished so much in making this world a better place. From any point of view, this world is made up of many types of cultures, races, and religions and although everyone is a member of a certain cluster we are all members of the human race. I was very lucky as a child to be born to an Italian man and a Chinese woman. Because of that special bond of love between my parents, I always wondered why others couldn't just get along with each other? I always wondered why people just couldn't look past race or religion and try to accept and understand others by who they are by their inner selves. I always wondered how our cultural differences could lead to Hatred and Racism between us?

Luckily, people have now come to understand the true meaning of Difference, Diversity and Multiculturalism.

It was through our education programs in schools and in our community centres, and through family discussions passed along at the dinner table, that people finally began to be willing to open their doors, which have been closed for so long, to diversity. Through this change of heart, people learned to share and accept the different cultures which make up our community. With this new knowledge, we, together, created a new and better way of living side by side.

By living in harmony, we have been able to stop racism in not just Ontario, and not just in Canada, but in all the world! Together we have not only improved our way of living, but have shown to the rest of the world that racism can be beaten. By coming to accept that our old ways were wrong we have been able to adapt to new ways of doing things. By living in harmony, we have created greater protection for all peoples who in the past had suffered from the evils of hatred and racism.

Multiculturalism allowed the people of Ontario to learn and grow as a united people. By living, sharing, and working together we made a great province even greater. In our unity, we have taught the rest of the world the beauty of racial peace and harmony. Thank you.

Alex Spinelli

Grade 7 / 7e année
Toronto District School Board

Fashion

Grade 7 / 7e année
Peel District School Board

Laura Flint

46

Stephanie Witten

Grade 12 / 12ᵉ année
Guido de Brès Christian High School
Hamilton

The Law and Scientific Ethics

When I consider my Ontario, all of Canada comes to mind. The province and the Country are inseparable. It is the provinces that come together to form the nation. Ontario is a wonderful member of the Canadian body. I am honoured to live here. Our large population and economic strength make for exciting possibilities and interesting surroundings. The history and heritage of Ontario have created a distinctive and strong province. But pride should not blind one's eye for weaknesses.

A true love for one's province and country demands that one never forgets the difficulties Ontario faces. We owe it to ourselves and the rest of Canada, never to ignore and refuse to acknowledge our problems. Once we take it for granted that Ontario's future is promising, we neglect our obligation to do all that's within our power to ensure the promises of the future become reality.

What I especially admire and wish to maintain about Ontario is that in general, the citizens can trust an orderly system of government and justice. At present the governments of many countries, including superpowers, are plagued by dishonesty and corruption. To me, the government and justice system a person lives under are important indicators as to their quality of life. A democratic and correct system of law and government means the difference between anarchy and order, tyranny and freedom. To maintain our present standard requires diligence, and improvement demands further constancy. When a system is good it is still not good enough. It is impossible to perfect human institutions but we must nevertheless exert all energy trying. Government, and specifically law, affect the lives of all Ontarians; that is precisely why those areas interest me. I know that I should not choose an occupation based primarily on what will make me happy but on what is for the good of society. God has granted me gifts and abilities not just for the sake of my own enjoyment and leisure, but to do what benefits my neighbour. By the year 2020

I feel that the legal system and laws of Ontario and Canada can be simplified and streamlined for the sake of clarity, efficiency and speed. As a lawyer I would like to contribute to the improvement of Canada's courts. There are brave new frontiers into which our laws must forge ahead. In our current age, scientific advancement and progress are occurring as quickly and as surely as time itself is moving forward. Already there are moral and ethical issues brought on by science, especially in the field of genetics. The privacy of genetic information from DNA will inevitably become of increasingly greater concern. Difficult cases involving custody of frozen embryos are becoming a reality. With the genuine possibility of human cloning, the legal implications are astounding, and the list goes on. It is my intention to enter into law with the express purpose of helping to regulate and control the use of technology. However, it must always be remembered that science itself isn't evil, it is how people decide to use science that needs legal reflection.

To allow science to operate without conscientious restraint or supervision would be foolhardy. The economic benefits of inventions or research should never compromise the rights and safety of Ontario's people. The future should not be feared. With the proper standards and regulations of conduct in the scientific community, there will be even less reason for anxiety over the unknown. No one can fully predict what breakthroughs may occur by 2020 and beyond, but I know that I want to be part of a legal system that is prepared for interesting and complex issues and is able to provide guidance. Improving Ontario's justice system in the area of scientific ethics would be of benefit to all of Canada. The notion of bettering the situation of my country and my fellow citizens is a heartening one. In all my plans I rest secure in the knowledge that God keeps our land strong and free. With that confidence I can look ahead with true optimism.

Mes pensées pour l'Ontario 2020

Je suis une étudiante de huitième année à l'école Sainte-Marguerite-Bourgeoys à Merrickville et je suis très bien éduquée. Mais quelquefois, je me demande si mes enfants vont être aussi bien éduqués que nous aujourd'hui. Est-ce que l'éducation va s'améliorer ou se détériorer? Est-ce qu'il va y avoir plus ou moins d'enfants ou d'adolescents dans les rues? Est-ce qu'il y aura des guerres en Ontario en l'an 2020? Qu'est-ce qui va arriver? C'est pour cela qu'on appelle ça le futur, on ne sait pas si notre province sera plus sécuritaire. Le savez-vous?

Quand je serai adulte, j'aimerais devenir enseignante pour les enfants ou les adolescents qui vivent dans les rues. J'aimerais leur enseigner les règles de la rue pour qu'ils puissent survivre et aussi leur donner une éducation pour qu'ils puissent avoir un emploi et avoir de l'argent pour être capables d'avoir de la nourriture et possiblement un gîte.

Quelquefois, je me demande s'il y aura des guerres en l'an 2020. J'ai peur, car en regardant les nouvelles, je vois le dommage que les guerres font aux villages, villes, maisons et gens. Je ne voudrais pas que ceci arrive à notre très belle province, l'Ontario.

Qu'est-ce qui va arriver en l'an 2020? Va-t-il y avoir des autos volantes, va-t-on découvrir les ovnis, vont-ils détruire notre futur? Il va falloir attendre l'an 2020 pour le savoir!

J'espère que les enfants et les adolescents de la prochaine génération vivront aussi bien que nous, les enfants et les adolescents d'aujourd'hui. J'espère énormément qu'il y aura moins de gens qui vivent dans les rues et qui sont sur l'assistance sociale et qu'ils ne passeront pas cette misère à leurs enfants de l'an 2020.

Ce qui ferait un monde meilleur, serait si les personnes qui sont riches verraient plus loin que leur fortune et si les gens de la loto réaliseraient qu'il y a des gens qui vivent dans les rues, des enfants et des adolescents qui font de la prostitution, et qu'il faut peut-être les aider un peu. Si on veut un monde meilleur, cela prendra très longtemps à obtenir. Si on veut que l'Ontario s'améliore, on doit s'entraider les uns les autres pour atteindre nos buts.

Pouvons-nous y arriver??? OUI!!!

Mélanie Bélanger

8e année / Grade 8
Conseil scolaire du district
catholique du Centre-Est de l'Ontario

Vision 2020 Class Project

Jiselle J.

Grade 1 / 1re année
Toronto Catholic
District School Board

49

Ontario 2020 we
will be kind to one
another like Jesus.

Sean O.

Grade 1 / 1re année
Toronto Catholic
District School Board

I'll help with the groceries.

50

Vision 2020 Class Project

I'll build churches.

Johnny D.

Grade 1 / 1re année
Toronto Catholic
District School Board

Sara K.

Grade 2 / 2e année
Toronto Catholic
District School Board

I will be kind like Jesus and be
kind to animals.

Vision 2020 Class Project

Jessica G.

Grade 1 / 1ʳᵉ année
Toronto Catholic
District School Board

51

I'll be a nurse and take care of others so they will not be sick.

Angus T.

Grade 2 / 2ᵉ année
Toronto Catholic
District School Board

I will work in a market so I can feed people.

52

Vision 2020 Class Project

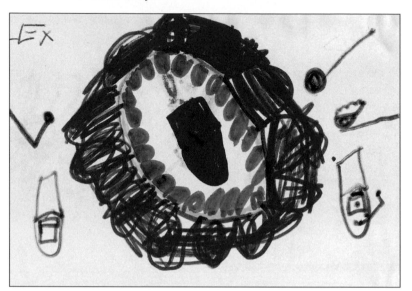

Alexandrina H.

Grade 1 / 1ʳᵉ année
Toronto Catholic
District School Board

I'll help people at church.

Arden S.

Grade 2 / 2ᵉ année
Toronto Catholic
District School Board

I will be a good team player
and play hockey.

Vision 2020 Class Project

Joanna F.

Grade 1 / 1ʳᵉ année
Toronto Catholic
District School Board

53

I'll teach others and they will be happy.

Christina A.

Grade 2 / 2ᵉ année
Toronto Catholic
District School Board

I will take my children to church for their First Communion.

54

Vision 2020 Class Project

Anastasia M.

Grade 1 / 1ʳᵉ année
Toronto Catholic
District School Board

I'll help people by
being a doctor.

Teresa P.

Grade 1 / 1ʳᵉ année
Toronto Catholic
District School Board

I will help children learn
more and talk about Jesus.

Vision 2020 Class Project

Cassandra C.

Grade 1 / 1ʳᵉ année
Toronto Catholic
District School Board

I will teach kids to brush their teeth.

Maggie K.

Grade 1 / 1ʳᵉ année
Toronto Catholic
District School Board

55

Vision 2020 Class Project

56

Dylan C.

Grade 1 & 2 / 1re et 2e année
Toronto Catholic
District School Board

I want to invent robots.

Julie T.

Grade 1 / 1re année
Toronto Catholic
District School Board

My Ontario will always
have good weather.

Vision 2020 Class Project

Tracey A.

Grade 1 / 1ʳᵉ année
Toronto Catholic
District School Board

57

When I am a vet I will take
care of the animals.

58

Doing My Part

By the year 2020 all the nations of the world will sign the "Letter of Universal Understanding," based on the principle that all the earth's people are entitled to and shall receive:

1) Sufficient food and potable water,
2) Adequate shelter and clothing,
3) Medical care,
4) Formal education,
5) Freedom to choose their own religion.

This will be the beginning of true peace on earth.

Signature: _____

Country: _____

Date: _____

I myself don't want to be an environmentalist but a surgeon. This doesn't mean that I won't do my part to create the Letter of Universal Understanding. One such way to create this is to send the cleanest water available in Canada to Third World countries. I pledge to spend my time creating the Letter of Universal Understanding and have it sent to our Canadian Prime Minister for signature.

Adam Sikora

Grade 8 / 8ᵉ année
Wellington Catholic
District School Board

Women's NHL Hockey

My Ontario
2020   Karolyn
                             McIlmoyle

In the year 2020 I am going to invent NHL women's hockey. I'm also going to allow body contact. I don't think it is fair for men to have body contact and not women. I hope to be one of the NHL players on one of these teams. Right now I am playing on a girls Rep team. I will try out for the NHL and hope to make it. In the year 2020 I am going to be 30 years old, old enough to play for the NHL. I am going to get together with many active women to make up some teams for the NHL. In this way I hope to have more equal opportunities for young Canadian women in Canada's National sport Hockey.

Grade 4 / 4e année
York Region District School Board

Karolyn McIlmoyle

My Community

My name is Megan Rose Monague. As a Native of North American ancestry, I have lived on Christian Island for all my life. In that time, I have been taught many things that show a relationship between me and my family, school, community, region, province, country, and the world. My favourite activities are: hockey and bike riding.

When I was little I often went to my Bup's house and sat with him and he often gave me half of his apple or orange and I usually didn't want the piece of fruit. I saw how much it meant to him so I took it. After that I went outside and I hung out with my older cousin Ray (who I worshipped and I rode his bike and felt like I was an invincible 15 years old). I felt like nothing could stop me and that growing up was so important to me. I felt like Ray (who was like an older brother to me) was one of those people. Now that my Bup and Ray are gone I feel that since I did that so often those memories are forever etched in my mind.

My family includes 34 first cousins. We are a very close family. We are very protective of each other. My family helps and supports any member of the family that decides to do something that they really want. My family has gone through so much in the past year that it somehow made us a very strong family and we are getting stronger every day. I am very proud of my family and I will do anything to help protect my younger cousins from things that they will regret in their life when they are older. I also like hanging out with my older cousins. They help me with things that I couldn't talk to anybody else about. They would give me insults, they help me with my homework and I look up to some of them as older brothers. I used to have a group of older cousins that would watch out for me and make sure that I was doing nothing illegal. Those boys would make sure that nothing would happen to me. I lost two of those boys and my whole family is helping each other cope with the void. We will continue to get stronger.

My community, of approximately one thousand inhabitants, is nestled along the southwest shore of Christian Island. I would consider our ferry and island "unique." We are one of the only communities that travel by a boat. We are also a very close-knit community. Each person on the island knows everybody by name. We all know how to relate to each other and we reach out to one another in a time of crisis. We also have the opportunity to swim on clean beaches and swim in clean water and go to any beach on our island without paying or worrying about any harmful garbage in our waters or our beaches. We also don't have to travel very far to go for a bike ride or go for a very lovely walk in the forests. We as Native people can also go fishing in our lakes and bays without worrying about being caught or paying a fine to put our boats in the water. I am glad that I live in Christian Island with my family and my friends.

My region is very unique because of the fur trade that formed in this area. Hundreds of years ago the fur trade was between the Natives and the Europeans. The Iroquois and the Huron people had their famous battle here that extinguished the Huron people's existence. This region also has Giant's Tomb; the legend has it that a giant had fallen into a deep sleep and will lie there forever. There was the Coldwater Experiment that started the idea for reserves. The Europeans knew that a reserve would work. Today people get jobs away from their homes. There are commuters that relocate from one place to another every day. This region is also unique because of the sand dunes. We try to preserve them because they are the only ones around this region.

The province of Ontario was once inhabited entirely by the Natives. Long ago the loyalists who came from Britain (and then a war broke out) settled here in Canada. There are the fish and land claims that make our province somewhat unique. Our province is also unique because we have a sense of culture. We all have respect for each person's race, gender or their sexual orientation.

My country of Canada is unique because we have very clean air. Our people in our country are very polite and helpful. Our country is a lot cleaner and we have very flat prairies and we produce a lot better fruits and vegetables and grains. We have gorgeous mountains. We also have very clean water – probably the cleanest water on the planet. Also, there is the French population. The French are very lucky because they are trying to preserve their language, and as Native people I understand that it is very hard to overcome.

Mother Earth is home to over five billion humans. The planet has a variety of features from the rugged mountains, hot dry deserts, to the deep blue oceans. The planet has a unique relationship with animals and its people. We as people must remember to respect our planet because it won't stay here forever.

My Ontario in the year 2020 will have seen grade eight transform itself into a teacher's degree, a four year term in teacher's college, or a law degree. I also see myself working on Christian Island full time or working in Midland as a hard working lawyer. I also would want a family after I have my career and I have my whole life planned out.

The region of Simcoe County will continue to enjoy the clean beaches and the fresh water. The County will also enjoy the skiing. Skiing will become more and more relaxing to a lot more people. The population in Ontario will in fact double but it won't become a problem. The schools in Simcoe County will get larger and they will have to build new schools.

Our country will become strong in the education department. Our students will graduate with honours. It will also become stronger in health

62

care. There will be more doctors and surgeons. The country of Canada will keep growing and there will be more electric cars. More and more industries will grow and our country will probably stay united.

I see myself, as a Native person in the year 2020, as a positive supporter in the rights for self-government. We would not have to depend on the Indian Affairs to handle our business any more. We as a community function better as an independent community. Our community in the year 2020 will still be using the ferry to go across. Our community will see how much we would need a sports complex for the youth.

The region of Simcoe County in 2020 will continue to have commuters to other areas of the country to work. The pollution will begin to be under more control; people will recycle and reuse and they will be more educated about how we are supposed to work with nature and not be trying to dominate the planet. The region will also enjoy more industries growing and bringing more profit into their towns.

The province of Ontario will also change in the year 2020. There will be an increase in immigration which, combined with the birth rate, could lead to a huge population. That would mean that Toronto will need more land and expand yet again. The Native economics will begin to change. More and more reserves would want to start a casino due to the fact that Rama is making a lot of profit and most of the Native peoples believe that Native people deserve a change. Bigotry in our province will become a forgotten issue. People in this province will no longer see color, they will see personality and humour.

Our country of Canada will stay united in the year 2020. Canada will realize how funny it will look if Quebec would separate. The country will continue to stay beautiful and become a getaway vacation to different people around the globe.

Megan Rose Monague   Christian Island Elementary School

63

L'an 2020 et son entourage

En l'an 2020 nous allons inventer une crème pour toutes les maladies. L'homme arrêtera de tuer les animaux. Les enfants autour du monde viendront en Ontario pour se faire enseigner dans une école. Tous les crimes arrêteront car nous allons inventer un système qui va leur dire d'arrêter. Il y aura plus de docteur. Il y aura beaucoup plus de jeunes dames qui seront des enseignantes. Les enfants vont acheter plus de livres pour lire et tous les êtres vivants auront un robot qui aide. Ce robot ne les laissera pas vieillir. En l'an 2020 l'Ontario sera sur Mars. Là nous n'allons pas mourir. Nous aimerons tout le monde de plus en plus et personne n'aura plus une seule allergie. Nous fabriquerons un crayon qui écrira par lui-même et des autos qui ne briseront jamais! En Ontario nous partagerons des maisons et même de l'argent! Il y aura beaucoup de choses mais ça peut arriver. Moi, je vais te revoir en 2020!

Pour réaliser mes rêves, je pourrai faire de la recherche et je pourrai aider les personnes à ne pas fumer. Je pourrai travailler à l'hôpital pour aider les docteurs. Je ferai un club qui inventera des inventions extraordinaires. Aussi nous nous ferons enseigner par un médecin et je pourrai être un scientiste pour guérir les animaux. J'aiderai les vieillards car je ramasserai tous les déchets par terre. Je vais aider une enseignante à enseigner la loi et à respecter le droit de l'enfant. J'aiderai les pompiers en ne commençant aucun feu et les policiers à résoudre un ou deux crimes en appelant les policiers si je vois un criminel. Et quand je trouverai du temps je garderai sûrement des enfants. J'espère que je trouverai le temps pour faire tout ça!

4ᵉ année / Grade 4
Conseil scolaire du district
du Grand Nord de l'Ontario

J. Tessier

64

Parler français

Il y a des personnes des autres pays qui viennent en Ontario pour parler français comme nous. En même temps il se feront de nouveau ami(e)s avec nous. Je suis certaine qu'il vont au moins se faire une ou un ami(e).

Ils iront à de bonnes écoles pour apprendre le français. Ils apprendront des choses extraordinaires comme nous.

Il y a toutes sortes de nouvelles familles qui viennent de tout partout. Ils viennent de la Chine, l'Afrique, l'Europe, île du Prince Édouard, etc. Ils viendront pour faire un voyage ou une visite, etc.

Gabrielle
4e et 5e année / Grades 4 & 5
Conseil scolaire du district catholique
de l'Est Ontarien

In the Year 2020...

In the year 2020 I think there will be new medication for cancer treatment. Everyone will have a home, money and good food. Fewer people will be poor.
   I will contribute to this happy condition whenever I can by donating money to the poor and for cancer research.

Brandon Bailey
Grade 3 / 3e année
District School Board
Ontario North East

65

When I Grow Up in 2020

When I'm grown up, in the year 2020, I would like to be an explorer!

by:

Grade SK / Jardin
York Region District School Board

Nick Munro

The Future of Ontario Class Project

J.
_____

66

I want to be a ballerina. I want to dance. I want everybody to watch me.

I want to be a cook. I want to mac pasta. I want to be a chief.

Sara
_____

Grade 1 / 1re année

The Future of Ontario Class Project

Luu Duc Minh Tri

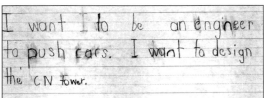

I want I to be an engineer to push cars. I want to design the CN tower.

I want to be a chef. I want to make a pizza.

Binh Vo

Grade 1 / 1re année

68

My Best Memories

One of my best memories in the province of Ontario is my trip to Wayne Gretzky's home town of Brantford, Ontario.

It took us about three hours to get there by automobile. When we got there we kept driving around to see the place because my parents and myself had never been there before.

The town itself was almost all farmland and fields. Gretzky's house is pretty much a farm. When you drive by, you can tell life revolves around hockey because there were three hockey nets, an ice rink and lots of sticks and pucks.

After we drove by his house we went to the first hockey arena he played in. They have a whole pro shop about him.

We were all hoping to get a tour of his house but it never happened. Nevertheless, we got to meet his proud father, Walter Gretzky. He was really nice and I got his autograph.

After that very long and tiring day we all went home. At least it was a lot of fun.

Yiorgo Christodoulou

Grade 7 / 7e année
Durham District School Board

69

With a Brave, True Heart

Ontario has achieved a lot since 1867 when it joined
in Canadian Confederation and I believe that in the
year 2020 we will carry through even more. We've
had our ups and downs but have always come out
with a brave, true heart. We have learned to accept
people for who they are instead of their colour,
culture or way of dressing, though we still have knots
to work out.

   In the year 2020 we will get rid of those knots and
turn Ontario into an extraordinary place with morals
and pleasures. I am convinced people will get along
and violence will be known as a legend. People will
not understand the term poverty because everyone
will be known as an equal. I imagine racism will be a
myth and everyone will join together with smiling
faces in happiness and joy. Education will be soaring
and technology will be at its best. Pollution will still
be around, but decreased.

   I know it sounds like a fantasy but if Ontario tries
hard enough I know we can accomplish anything
and everything.

Grade 8 / 8ᵉ année
Toronto Catholic District School Board

Sharda Manny

70

I Wonder

In the Year 2020 I wonder how it will be?
Will there still be wars,
Famine, and deadly diseases?

In the Year 2020 Ontario would see change
Political, Economic and Social.
Will people care?
Or will we be caught up in our own affairs?
Will there be clones,
And more high-tech cellphones?

In the Year 2020 where would the young be?
Would they be homeless?
Is there a place for you and me?
Would our government be true to their word?
Or uttering things absolutely absurd!

In the Year 2020 would Quebec have self rule?
Would people of colour find the tools
Needed to accomplish their goals?
Like the winter kills the flower,
Will our history be forgotten?
How can this be?
In the Year 2020 I wonder how things will be?

Erich S. Hagley

Grade 7 / 7ᵉ année
Toronto District School Board

Science and Technology
La science et la technologie

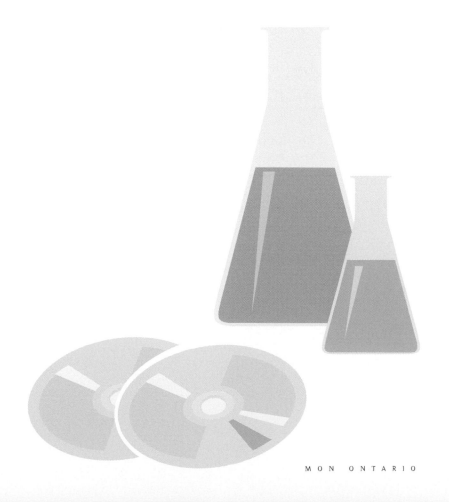

72

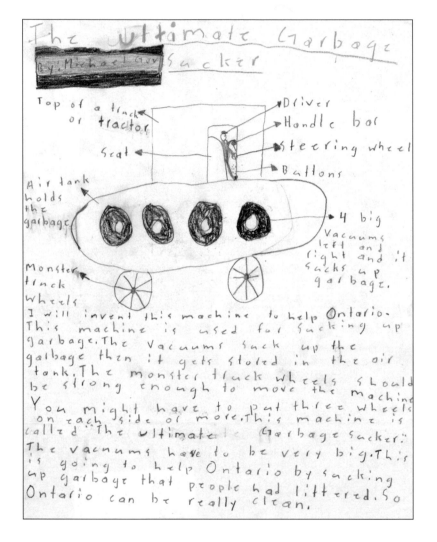

The Ultimate Garbage Sucker

I will invent this machine to help Ontario. This machine is used for sucking up garbage. The vacuums sucks up the garbage then it gets stored in the air tank. The monster truck wheels should be strong enough to move the machine. You might have to put three or more wheels on each side. This machine is called "The Ultimate Garbage Sucker." The vacuums have to be very big. This is going to help Ontario by sucking up garbage that people have littered so Ontario can be really clean.

Michael Gov

Grade 3 / 3e année
Toronto District School Board

Research to Find Causes for Diseases

This is my idea for my Ontario 2020. I would like to see more research for the causes of disease. (That doesn't mean research scientists are not doing a good job already.) These are the suggestions I thought of for doctors to raise money for better research for causes of some diseases that don't have a cause yet.

The suggestions I thought of include having a bingo night with prizes or have a few puppet shows. Other suggestions involve magic shows, car washes, and sell books about terrible diseases, (to people who have one), so they know what their disease does and they won't be so worried.

By doing this, maybe in twenty years doctors will have at least a few causes for some diseases with no causes yet.

With more causes for diseases less people will get sick, because they'll avoid the causes. Less people will die too because they'll avoid the causes for diseases that can't be cured.

This is what I think the doctors should do for better research for some diseases. That is my Ontario 2020.

Grade 4 / 4ᵉ année
Peel District School Board

Stephen Malesevich

Real or Imaginary

In the middle of the picture, there is a woman wearing a simulation suit which is the 2020's technology and is manufactured in Ontario. The suit serves many purposes. It can bring its wearer to a computerized virtual world. The suit has a slot where discs can be inserted. The disc contains every detail of the computerized virtual world. The computerized world can be anywhere. On the top left corner of the picture, the woman is experiencing what it's like to be Juliet in Shakespeare's "Romeo and Juliet." On the bottom, the woman is experiencing being an astronaut. On the top right corner, the woman is experiencing what it's like to play Maria in "The Sound of Music." In the computerized virtual world, the person can still touch and feel, but the people involved are holograms.

This technology will bring people a lot of convenience. Although it will cut down job opportunities, this invention will also create new jobs. With this new technology, people don't have to buy furniture, silverware, or decorations for their home anymore. They can program their home to look like whatever they want it to be, and it will last forever unless they want to change it. People don't have to go to other countries to see the sights for vacation, they can buy discs of California sunshine, and the whole family can go to California. This suit can also be used for educational purposes. For instance, when students are studying Shakespeare's play, instead of reading the text that sometimes causes difficulties for the readers, they can just buy the program and experience the whole play for themselves. They don't even have to memorize anything because the experience will stay in their minds forever. Also, in a history class, the events can be written into programs and they will help the students understand the different perspectives and what it feels like to experience those situations.

With the help of this new technology, the crime rate will be reduced because people's desires are satisfied in their own virtual worlds. The programs also have a safety device attached to it. It can control the degree of injury. When things get too violent and dangerous, the program will automatically shut down to ensure the user's safety.

This technology is likely to be developed because right now we are already capable of creating multipath movies which let the viewers become the directors. Also we are capable of creating life experience simulations (e.g., Imax 3-D films). Combining these two technologies with some more improvement will make this whole picture come true.

This technology is terrific, but it will also create new kinds of problems that we have never encountered before. Just like the convenience of the Internet and how it can be falsely used. One of the problems that might occur is that the programs might be too perfect for the users that they will like to stay in the virtual world and refuse to return to the reality. People may become so dependent on this technology that all the other wonderful things in life may be ignored. Then there is going to be a real problem. Not minding all the others, this will stop the further improvement of our society and the whole of humanity.

Grade 9 / 9e année

Amy Yu-Chieh Hu

Advanced Technology

In the future, I predict that Ontario will change dramatically. An increase in population will cause lust for innovation to become more evident, as new and newer machines are being invented. Many new innovations will help to make the people of Toronto and Ontario's jobs much less straining than imagined.

Robots, some miniature and some gargantuan, will run the communities of tomorrow. A robot popcorn dispenser at the movies, a robot info-terminal in the stores. Who knows, maybe a robot teacher may teach the classrooms of tomorrow! Robot-operated cranes will build our houses and offices, and microscopic nanobots will cruise our bloodstream, destroying all infecting viruses. In fact nanotechnology, the power to manipulate molecules with extremely small robotics, will push the technology level to the limits. Computer chips will be measured in nanometres instead of millimetres; computers will become amazingly small and portable. In fact, I think the 2020 computer will be the size of a Gameboy™ and the graphics will be as breathtakingly 3D as N64™, and possibly better. There is a chance that robots will become small enough to squeeze into a cell and alter the human chromosomes. If we could make enough "nano-zappers," eventually we could eliminate the aging gene completely. Once you're born, you could never die of old age!

The bus drops you off from school and you walk to the door. There's no keyhole and the door is locked! Just grab the door and wait five seconds as the computer scans your finger and handprint. *Whoosh!* The door opens. You place your bag on a hanger and grab a Virtual Reality (VR) helmet. You ask the computer for a snack and a robot arm delivers it. You plug the helmet into the NVR console and insert *Super Mario Brothers VR™*. Welcome to the home of the future! Old TV sets will be replaced by newer, Virtual Reality systems. Place the helmet on your head and, using a miniaturized HUD (Heads-Up-Display), you'll be able to watch "TV"! Nodding your head upward increases the volume, nodding it down decreases it. To change channels, just move your head to the left or right. Motion detectors mounted on the helmet will respond to your every movement and react accordingly. Video game systems will be replaced with these as well, however, instead of using traditional keypads, these same sensors will detect where your hands are at all times. It will feel like you're in the game! This will be virtual reality, and if it becomes cheaper than dating, the human race is doomed.

While eating your snack, you walk up the stairs to your bedroom and flip open your laptop. Most schools will use laptops for work, as opposed to wasting paper. You'll take your laptop home and finish your homework, then bring it back to school the next day. This will be much easier for the students, as homework can't get lost. If work becomes lost or misplaced, the computer will easily find it using a "find" command. At school, desks will be a thing of the past. Students will sit in chairs with a small HUD in front of them, and plug the laptop into the chair to download assignments. Sitting in a virtual "classroom," a teacher, using another one of these chairs, will explain what you need to know and then save the files onto your laptop. Any assignments that are supposed to be handed in will be saved to the main computer as soon as your class begins. At the end of class, your assignment will be handed back, all graded. Almost all classes will be taught this way, and it shall be much more efficient. However, the only class not taught in this fashion will be gym. Despite all technology, it is still impossible to achieve physical fitness without engaging in a physical activity. It shall be taught the same way as it is now.

Ontario will not be much of a province without a way to get around. However, a population boom will create a problem with our current technology. A regular car produces too much smog, so in the future, cars and buses and trucks will have to become much cleaner. They will no longer run on petroleum, but on hydrogen. Already there are several cars and three buses that run on eco-friendly fuel cells. In the future, probably the only problem with our cars will be over watering, as the only by-product of fuel cells is the famed H_2O, otherwise known as water. This will solve two problems; it will solve the over-pollution problem and will provide water to the countries that do not have much. There will be very few diesel and electric trains in the future. Instead, many of them will be replaced with either the aerotrain or magnetic levitation trains. The aerotrain is essentially a hovercraft on a track, and the maglev train uses magnets to hover above the track. Both will be extremely fast, as both operate in a frictionless environment. However, these will be quite expensive, although not as expensive as an airline ticket.

The airlines of the future are going to be relatively fast and comfortable compared to today's versions. It still won't be possible for civilians to travel into space yet, but it *will* become easier for astronauts to travel about. Already, scientists and inventors are discovering new ways to put a rocket into space. One theory, which would be used for placing small satellites into orbit, would be a "laser-propelled ship." Focus a laser into a highly polished cone, and the air heats up and causes a mini-explosion. This propels a craft forward. Another theory is to use a nuclear engine. However, because of radiation, this would have to be built, piece by piece, in space. Also being pondered is the use of a "swing." A platform then would pick up the cargo, swing it around and then let it go. Since there is no gravity and no friction in space, an object will keep moving. Another platform will "catch" the load and place it on the ground.

Medical advances are being made each day, yet, little by little, illnesses are invading our bodies. It will be easy to cope in the future, in comparison to today, but we still won't have cures for everything. Nano-robots will be able to save many lives, but unfortunately, they will most likely be expensive operations. And there's more bad news: slowly our bodies are becoming immune to penicillin, the substance used to soothe colds. We'll begin to die from the common cold again.

Natural resources won't become a problem in the year 2020, as Mother Earth still has much metal and wood. However the Earth will begin to run dry on oil, and it can't create any more coal, so we shall have three main options for replacing our fossil fuel problem. One is to create a totally new substance using particles of others. Two is to stop using the materials altogether and three is to use nanotechnology to change existing molecules into the pieces needed. Option one would solve the problem, but would this substance be all-purpose, cheap, flexible or hard? Option two we would already be working on. Fuel cell-operated cars don't need fossil fuels to run. Option three would work very well, as it is easier and much more cost effective.

The future is most likely to become quite expensive, but we'll begin to be paid much more. This is because, as price increases with technology, companies can afford to pay employees more. With a little work, and some great technology, our lives can become much cleaner, safer, and easier.

Making these predictions come true is difficult, but many of these technologies are being used or designed today, though they are still in the testing stage. I am quite interested in a technology field of work for my career and I might be the one that implements the use of this technology. I will conserve our resources and try to vote for the man/woman who will keep our province clean, cautious and cool!

Grade 7 / 7e année
Sommerville Manor Private School
Mississauga

Peter Kucirek

Earth Day 2020

I will invent vehicles that keep the planet clean. By: Keegan Dunn

78

Keegan Dunn

Grade 2 / 2ᵉ année
Dufferin-Peel Catholic
District School Board

L'auto du futur

Il va peut-être avoir des nouvelles sortes d'autos. Je prédis que les nouvelles sortes d'autos auront une mini fusée de vent et il va y avoir 7 sièges et une toilette et le plancher sera en bois franc. Les sièges seront de velour. Il va y avoir une mini télévision. Au dessus, il y aura des trous qui feront sortir le vent. L'auto pourrais se changer en bateau et la mini fusée de vent seras bloquée et si tu fait quelque chose comme se moucher ou aller à la salle de bain, il y auras un ordinateur qui conduira pour toi et un robot pour te servir si tu as faim et 97 sacs gonflable qui sortira si tu crash.

79

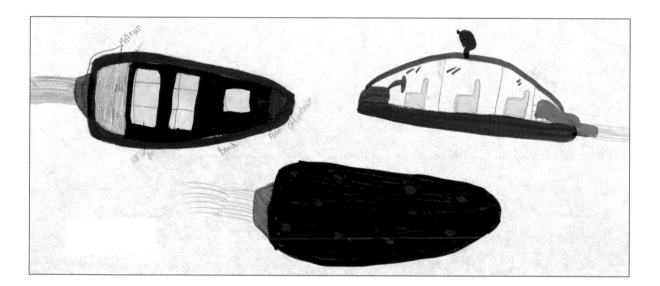

5e année / Grade 5
Conseil scolaire du district catholique
de l'Est Ontarien

Benoit Viau

Daily Life in 2020

80

Daily Life in ONTARIO 2020

In Ontario school's there will be laptop's to learn on and the computer's will talk to you. (Computer's would be like teachers) The desks will have buttons so you can push to make your lunch, work books, pencils, markers, crayons; etc.

Our homes will have robotic buttlers that are programmed to do whatever you tell them. Everybody will have arcades, nintendos, gameboys; etc. There will be elevators to get up and down the house. Kids will have motorized skateboards. The homes might be quadruple deck houses. Everybody will have go-carts for cars.

Instead of telephones everybody would have PC's. **WHAT IS A PC!** A PC is a telephone with a camera so people could see each other.

Grade 5 / 5e année
District School Board
Ontario North East

Keith Peckover

Une vision de la vie dans le futur

La plupart des choses dans mon dessin représentent des aspects technologiques possibles pour l'avenir. Par exemple, les piscines sur les toits et les terrains de stationnement à trois étages montrent qu'avec les populations qui augmentent, l'espace sera de plus en plus précieux. Les hélicoptères, les trains magnétiques (et les rues) illustrent les diverses façons de voyager. À cause de la pollution, nous utilisons des moyens non-polluants comme des panneaux solaires (sur satellites) et des éoliennes (qui utilisent le vent) pour nous procurer de l'électricité et de l'énergie. Le dôme à octogone n'est pas encore inventé. Cela aussi existe déjà et à cause de sa structure, on peut l'utiliser pour plusieurs fonctions. La communication est aussi représentée par les satellites, mais ce qui est important c'est l'emplacement de l'école. Elle est placée au milieu. Ceci montre que l'éducation devient de plus en plus important et que nous avancerons sur les plans médical, technologique, environnemental… Bref, nous évoluerons ensemble en tant qu'espèce humaine.

9ᵉ année / Grade 9   **Rachäel Smith**

The Year's 2020

The year's 2020 and I'm 34,
I just sent my 8 year old son out the door.
But before he left he said he had something to say,
"Were vehicles electrically powered in your day?"
I replied, "No, son, they were powered by gasoline,
But they switched to electricity so the air is now clean."

I stood standing for a second then heard quite a loud "ring,"
Someone was calling me on the picture phone,
my business partner, Don Tsing.
He told me to get dressed and be at the office by 9:00,
I had a business meeting and should be there on time.
See, I design computers, which help you around the house,
They clean, they cook, they organize all without a mouse.

As I drove along the narrow street in my fast electric car,
I realized our progress the last 20 years had got us quite far,
And then I remembered back 20 years ago,
When I was a junior high student with nowhere to go.
One day in English class we were working on a project,
About the year 2020, Ontario and how they connect.
I was writing a poem about what Ontario would be like,
And guess what…I was right.

Ryan Morrice

Grade 8 / 8e année
Toronto District School Board

85

In the Future

In the future, I hope they make some flying cars. Or a bike with twenty wheels and some flying people. And toys that can talk to you and pets that can talk back to you. I would also like to see a time capsule that would take me back in time. Then I could see people in the past and the way they lived in the past. In the future if gravity was changed, I could jump 10 feet in the air. I would like to meet Jesus in the future. I would like to see fruit made out of chocolate, too, and people lived for peace forever.

Grade 2 / 2e année
London District Catholic School Board

Patrick Donnelly

The Busy Day of 2020

Here it is the year 2020 and as a thirty year old businesswoman, I am about to begin my day. My talking computer has just informed me that it is 5 a.m. and it is a warm and sunny day in Ottawa.

I reach for my remote control and program into my computer my menu for breakfast. Healthy food and my vitamin pill will give me the energy I need for my busy day. My robot should have it prepared for me in about fifteen minutes.

I climb out of bed, walk into my large walk-in closet and reach for my dressy blue shorts and my silky white blouse. Usually I stay home with my business but I am dressing up today because I have to make a presentation to a new computer company.

I walk into my elevator and it takes me downstairs. My breakfast is ready for me to eat, thanks to my helpful robot. After I finish eating I hop into my elevator and it takes me to my office in my basement. I turn on my business computer and review my information for my presentation. Before leaving for my meeting I give instructions to my robot for the day. Laundry and housecleaning will be done while I am away.

Next I hop into my car and program the car computer to take me to my meeting. The streets are busy with fast moving cars. My talking car computer tells me about an accident nearby, so we take a different route than expected. I pass by my old school where children are playing outside. It must be recess time. Their school days begin at 7 a.m. and finish at 7 p.m. so they have a few outdoor breaks. They now enjoy year round schooling, which is different from when I went to school.

My work day has been busy and I return home at 5 p.m. I change into my tights and T-shirt and go to my neighbourhood health club for my workout. Fitness is a very important part of my day. I see many of my friends at the club and we arrange to meet at our neighbourhood restaurant for dinner at 8 p.m.

I return home after dinner and relax for a while. I listen to my stereo before going to bed. My robot has been busy and the house is clean and my bed is now ready for me to go to sleep. It has been a busy day as usual, and I go to bed around midnight. Tomorrow will be another busy day!

Amanda Hoskin

Grade 5 / 5ᵉ année
Ottawa-Carleton District School Board

Les autos-robots

Imagine un jour tu te lèves et il y a des robots qui marchent, des autos qui voyagent seul. Ça, ça m'est arrivé. Je me suis levée un matin pour trouver tout ça.

Les autos voyageaient sur des aimants dans les rues. On avait juste besoin de choisir où on allait. Les autos-robots sont meilleures pour conduire que les humains!

Les robots aidaient les humains en nettoyant la maison et en faisant des bâtiments. Les robots pouvaient faire des choses que les humains ne peuvent pas faire.

J'ai appris beaucoup de cette aventure et je ne peux pas attendre l'arrivée de l'an 2020.

87

4e année / Grade 4
Ottawa-Carleton District School Board

Samantha Buttemer

I Wonder...

I wonder what the world will be like in the year 2020? Who will be running our lives: robots, computers, aliens or us?

You don't often see a robot these days, but in 2020, you will probably see robots working at supermarkets, in the factories or even driving the buses and trains.

The airplanes will be larger and faster than before. Now, for example, the travel time from Toronto to India is 22 hours. However, the super-sonic jets will take us to India in just 10 hours.

Now, whenever you enter in your house, you usually turn on your lights, but in 2020 you might not have to do that. Your house would be computerized by sound. Instead, all you would have to say is, "Lights on," and the lights would be on.

You could also buy a fridge that reminds you what to buy; for example, whenever you open the fridge door, it would tell you whether you are running out of milk or if you do not have any bread left. It would be very common to have a telephone with a screen; you could talk to the person face to face.

Where would be the perfect place to go during your vacation? Perhaps Moon. (If only people could afford it.)

In the next millennium, perhaps every household will have a computer, which will make it easier for the teachers to send the students their report cards by e-mail instead of handing the hard report, and more people will be working from home.

Cars of the future would be running by solar energy and electricity.

Although we will be living in a computer age in the world and in Ontario, we should make Ontario the cleanest, safest and pollution free.

We can make Ontario more welcoming to our visitors by being polite, helpful, and kind. We should try to be a good ambassador to our visitors.

We can make Ontario more safe by not selling drugs. We should have a stiffer penalty for anyone who commits a crime.

We can make Ontario pollution free by having a minimum of car use and using bikes as transportation. We should have a smoke free environment There should be heavier fines or even jail terms if they find any company dumping chemicals into the lakes or rivers.

We should inform the government that, instead of spending money on weapons, it should be spent on health, education and the environment. My visions for 2020:

a) there is enough food and shelter for everyone in Ontario so there aren't any homeless people on the streets,
b) that there will be a cure for cancer and other diseases that can kill people,
c) and people are still kind enough to share.

Sonal Chopra

Grade 6 / 6e année
Toronto District School Board

Helping Dogs

> My Ontario 2020
> In the year 2020 I'm going to be a vet and invent dog pills that taste like doggie biscuits and help dogs from getting cancer.
>
> Me
>
> Pills that taste like doggie biskets
>
> VET
>
> Sick dog
>
> Elise Fullerton age 7
>
> Lorne Park Public School

Grade 2 / 2ᵉ année
Peel District School Board

Elise Fullerton

90

The Best Ever

In the year 2020 I will be 31 years old. I would like to be a scientist when I grow up. I might even have a family by then, I don't know. I would relish the idea to have homes for the homeless. The government should supply them with some money, clothes, food and even some furniture for the house.

I would also wish that we could find cures for AIDS, Cancer and other life threatening ailments. I think that women should be able to be the Prime Minister of Canada or other leaders of authority.

Wouldn't it be a wonderful thing to have a flushing garbage can! Maybe someone might have invented one by then, what do you think? Astronauts might even be able to go to different planets and see if there's any life out there. If there was life on other planets it would be cool. They could take pictures of the aliens so that everyone else would be able to see what they look like.

In the year 2020 there might even be $5 coins. It wouldn't be much fun having to carry coins around all the time. If we did have all these coins, someone should invent a special wallet to carry them in.

You might even be able to see the person on the telephone. If you could see the person on the other line, without them seeing you, and you don't know who it is you do not have to answer it.

I think my Ontario 2020 is going to be the best millennium ever.

Sandra Trimm   Grade 5 / 5ᵉ année
                                     Peel District School Board

Our World

For the year 2020 we have designed and created three new vehicles on a scale starting from a mini-mail to an off ground explorer. These vehicles consist of batteries and solar power, which would be used for the new millennium.

We added different high tech, advanced technology to our vehicle. Features we have added to the vehicle are the television set that Ashley, Mandy and Divani's group has put together. It is a 13 inch model television, which has four screens that you can view. Instead of having a remote control to change the channels they have decided to make it voice activated. If you wanted to change the channel, you would speak to the television and it would move to that channel. Another entertainment value would be the mini-CD player, which would also be voice activated. You would load in the CDs and then say which one you wanted to listen to. We wanted the vehicles to be water and fire resistant, which would protect the car from getting rusted and chip the paint. We also wanted the car to be safe so we added air bags for all the passengers. In the back the air bags would come out of the seat in front of the passengers. The vehicle that we have created would be able to fly, float in the water and drive on land.

Our other vehicle would be a skateboard where there would be no need for leg movement. The skateboard, like our other vehicle, would be radio-controlled and fly with jetpacks. To use the vehicle you would put it flat on the ground, step on top of it and voice activate it to start. This will be another way of transportation in the year 2020.

Our last idea was well thought through. It is called a mini-mail. The mini-mail would be a computerized plane that took over the mail carrier. It would transport mail to people in alphabetical order and by the area you lived in. It would drop off small packages and envelopes to people's houses. However, the mini-mail would not be able to deliver big packages to people.

Our project has hopefully given you an idea of what we think it will be like in the year 2020. As you probably heard in our presentation, our project has shown a great deal of voice activation. Two of the three ideas we talked about were run by voice activation. We think that this will be one of the many creative devices of the new millennium.

Amanda
Bhavjit Hansra
Natalie Toney

92

A Piggyback Song

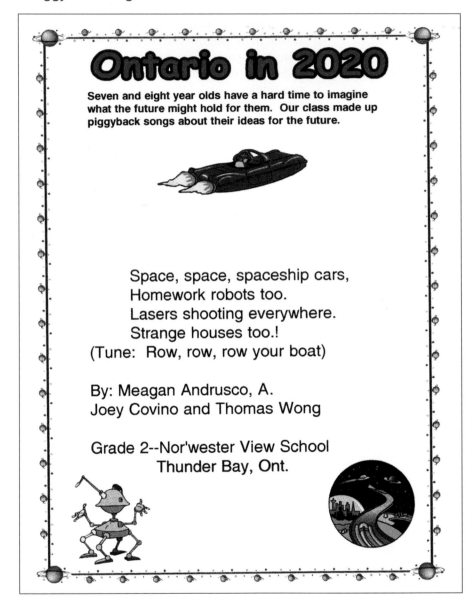

Ontario in 2020

Seven and eight year olds have a hard time to imagine what the future might hold for them. Our class made up piggyback songs about their ideas for the future.

Space, space, spaceship cars,
Homework robots too.
Lasers shooting everywhere.
Strange houses too.!
(Tune: Row, row, row your boat)

By: Meagan Andrusco, A.
Joey Covino and Thomas Wong

Grade 2--Nor'wester View School
Thunder Bay, Ont.

Thomas Wong
Joey Covino
Meagan Andrusco
A.

Lakehead District School Board

What I Think Ontario Will Be Like in 2020

What I Think Ontario will Be Like in 2020.

I think that there will be pencils that you tell what you want to write and they will write it down for you. I also think that they will have doors that will open for you. and have your name for the lock number. And transportation will be easier than it is now because they will have cars that drive by themselves. And the lights will turn on with the clap of your hands. And thats it. Robots will do do your home work for you too.

WH. Ballard School   by Amanda Bettencourt
Miss German - Teacher   Grade 3

Grade 3 / 3e année
Hamilton-Wentworth
District School Board

Amanda Bettencourt

Classrooms in the Year 2020

94

I am going to become a teacher and I plan on being an inventor on the side. I want to do this so teachers don't have to worry about not enough space in the room because you can ~~lower the other~~ another layer of kids over one, and they don't have to worry about chalk and all that. And then the kids don't have to buy notebooks they just use the computer.

Shannon Gayle George

Grade 6 / 6e année
Northwest Catholic
District School Board

SPM8

Spm 8 is my new robot for the new millenium. He is going to be used in the future for garbage collection. He will clean up the streets, and the beaches the parks. The earth will be free of garbage

Grade 2 / 2ᵉ année
Superior North Catholic
District School Board

Steven P. McParland

My Postage Stamp of Ontario

I am a scientist inventing more ways to use wind and solar energy.

96

Allen Wywrot

Grade 1 / 1ʳᵉ année
Thunder Bay Catholic
District School Board

Après la bombe 34R, la vie est définitivement bonne!

Bip, bip, mon réveil sonne à sept heures tous les jours. Je suis trop fatiguée pour commencer d'organiser toutes mes choses pour la journée. Mais je devais aller au travail, alors je me suis levée de mon lit.

Quand j'étais prête, j'ai pris une auto-robot à l'hôpital. Quand je me suis rendue à mon pupitre, j'ai vu qu'il y avait juste quatre bilans. C'était comme ça depuis à peu près quatre mois maintenant. Parce que depuis le moment où tous les remèdes pour les maladies les plus importantes étaient donnés aux victimes, l'hôpital ne prenait que des rendez-vous pour les bilans annuels. Quand ces remèdes avaient été introduits, tout le monde était heureux, spécialement moi, car j'étais une des personnes qui travaillaient sur un des remèdes. Et on l'a trouvé par accident, un accident qui a tué plus d'un million de vies.

Près de la fin de la troisième guerre mondiale, quand les extraterrestres de Jupiter ont laissé tomber la bombe 34R sur notre pays et sur tous les autres pays autour du monde, les gaz qui venaient de la bombe ont contaminé la nourriture des villes très loin d'où ils venaient. Un homme qui a mangé cette nourriture et avait une tumeur cancéreuse a été guéri. On a fait d'autres tests et on a trouvé que quand ces produits chimiques étaient mélangés avec d'autres substances, ils formaient d'autres sortes de remèdes pour d'autres maladies.

Après mes quatre bilans, qui étaient tous le matin, je suis allée travailler sur mon ordinateur. Je suis encore stupéfiée par la technologie maintenant. Car je n'utilisais pas beaucoup les ordinateurs avant de commencer mon travail. Les ordinateurs contrôlaient toutes les écoles, les usines et même beaucoup d'émissions de télévision et d'autres sortes d'amusements.

Après mon travail, je suis allée à un petit restaurant pour avoir du café et pour lire mon livre. J'ai demandé du café à la serveuse électronique. C'était très calme et silencieux dans le restaurant et il y avait beaucoup de personnes dedans, et plusieurs adolescents. La vie était très paisible depuis 20 ans! Parce qu'après la guerre, tout le monde s'est rendu compte que la violence était horrible et après du temps, il n'y a plus eu de violence.

Oui, les choses se sont certainement améliorées dans le temps, mais la seule chose qui est encore un problème mondial est la pollution. Mais j'ai entendu dire que commençant cette année, il y aura un programme concernant la pollution qui va mettre fin à ce problème.

La vie est définitivement bonne!

8e année / Grade 8
Toronto District School Board

Jennifer Anglin

98

Pur et propre

Beaucoup plus propre.
Les gens utilisent des poubelles au lieu de jeter
leurs déchets par terre.
Nos parcs seront des endroits immenses.
Plus d'activités récréationnels seront à l'extérieur.

Julie Zabizewski   8e année / Grade 8
Conseil scolaire du district catholique
Centre-Sud

I Predict . . .

99

My Ontario In The Year 2020

In the year 2020, I think life will be very different. There will be more advanced technology that will help us find cures for medical problems and produce better health equipment. By the year 2020, I predict that students will be "going" to school by sending e-mails on the laptop computers that they will have. Teachers will teach them through cyberspace. Cars will not run on fuel; they will run on water which will make it easier for drivers, since they wouldn't have to stop for gas. Cars would also look a little different. Bigger with more features They will have the ability to travel anywhere; On land, water and even air. Many new spieceis of animals will be discovered and they will be so intelligent and powerful, humans will let them control the world. House would look different and everyone will have cable T.V. Movie theaters will have bigger, wider screens. Buildings will be structured differently, more fancier. Prices will be cheaper and no one will pay taxes. No one will be poor and everyone will live in peace and harmony Everyone will be 100% smarter. This is how I think my Ontario will be in the year 2020.

100

City Life

I think Ontario will have changed a great deal by the year 2020. Maybe for the better or maybe for the worse. My picture portrays what I think Toronto might look like in the year 2020.

With all the technology we have now, we can do almost anything. Just imagine what 2020 will be like! We'll have restaurants and highways thousands of feet up in the air, the CN Tower won't be the world's tallest structure anymore, cars will use water instead of gas, people will just have to touch a screen to navigate a vehicle. It will be commonplace for a car to come equipped with a TV and a phone! These are just some of the many possibilities! Wouldn't even more technology advancements be fun and at the same time useful in the year 2020?

I think that there will be a lot more technology in 2020. I chose to draw a picture of the changes made to a city in the span of 20 years or so because I thought it would really portray my vision of Ontario in 2020. I thought that a before and after picture showing changes made to a city would show technological advances very well. "City Life" really shows the difference from now (1999) and what I think Toronto might look like in 2020.

I think that Ontario in 2020 will be better than it is now (at least I hope so!). I know that there will be more violence, poverty and discrimination, but I also know that Ontario will work hard to stop that. Overall, I know that Ontario will be a better place in 2020, but that still leaves the question, what will 2020 be like?

101

Grade 7 / 7ᵉ année
Peel District School Board

Neeru Sekhon

My Future Ontario

102

103

I think my Ontario in the year 2020 will be filled with all sorts of different technology and inventions.

I am going to paint and put in little details with pastel. The reason for doing that is because paint did not seem right for doing really fine details. It will make the picture have more eye-catching colours for its viewers.

My focal point is the landmark of Ontario. The most common landmark of Ontario, of course, the one and only tallest building ever made called the CN Tower. It will make everyone know that this picture is for Ontario and not for British Columbia or Manitoba.

I chose the shape of the cars like that because it makes it look different from the cars now. They look more advanced with a higher type of technology and power. I put lights on the road because now some accidents happened because of vision problems or they didn't see the sign because it was too dark so they came up with this idea. Now in the year 2020 no one can say, "I couldn't see because of the darkness," or any other excuse about how dark it is. Of course, in the year 2020 the Canadian dollar will be worth more than it is now in order to put lights. The taxes will be raised in the year 2020. So will the ages of when you can get your driver's license!

My role in the year 2020 will be my normal life, except there will be a few changes, like when I get my driver's license, and the different models of cars. And also, I forgot to mention all the extra jobs that will be open for young people like me.

Grade 7 / 7e année
Peel District School Board

Mandeep Gavria

What I Think It Will Be Like in Ontario in the Year 2020

In the year 2020 I think the world will be a bit cleaner than before, or a lot dirtier! As I see it, we will either get better, or a lot worse. Even now when we are trying to clean up, I think we might have permanently gotten the Earth dirty forever.

The space station that a few countries are building together will either be finished, and people will be living in it, or it will have some malfunctions and explode, or an airlock will break off, the computer might even go offline on the station. What I keep coming to, is that this is a big turning point for us. We could make some big breakthrough or we could crash and burn.

As for all those myths about "flying cars," well surprise, surprise! We already have them, in fact we had them before 1970, when Hovercrafts were made. They both have the same basic design for their engines, except one is more powerful because it is going to haul a boat around.

About the industries then. McDonald's will probably still be the richest fast food restaurant on the planet. Japan and China will still be big producers of toys and plastic, some new computer tech stores will most likely have shown up and have all kinds of stuff to sell, lightning balls will probably be $10.00 instead of $50.00.

I think that when you are born, doctors will put an implant on or in your brain that will give you all that you need to know. All you need to do is choose what you want to be when you grow up, then it will give you the required information for that job! And for kids, that means what? If you answered NO SCHOOL you're right!

In the way of television, I think that it will get unpopular and after a while the TV network will be closed down entirely. Instead of television we will have an LCD panel with an outlet for a high-tech VCR, and a video slot to play your tapes, because the VCR would be like a memory for favorite channels, programmed timeslots that you want to see, and a (the usual) clock.

After the talk about TV, I think that it would not be complete without a bit on Nintendo, Sega, and other systems. I think that they will enhance to a point that they are 3D, and you are actually the person, you wouldn't feel the pain of course but you would feel the fire, water, wind, or whatever there is in the game. You would also feel it if something in the game brushed you or pushed you. No pain, but still a feeling.

The houses that we live in will change too. Maybe they will be a sphere that glows and can only be opened by certain people...by walking through! It would only let family members in, or friends that you program to get in. As I see it, this would all work by genes, blood types, molecules, etc.

I would think that money would be of little, if any use at all. Instead we might use energy for money. For example, you work and you earn energy (electricity or whatever the new stuff, if anything new at all). The energy is used to power things, and it would be like trading, energy for a kangaroo doll that walks and insults your sister or brother. The salesmen/saleswomen would take the energy and spend it or use it.

In twenty-one years there has to be something besides burgers, maybe something called Grog that looks like eyeballs! If that happens, then they had better find a way to change the stuff's appearance. Eyeballs for breakfast, yuck! If the eyeballs tasted good, people might try them and never again, because face it folks, people would get grossed out if they ate a food that looked like eyeballs.

Cancer, AIDS, Multiple Sclerosis, Smallpox, the Measles. These are all diseases that are around here. Sure Smallpox has been contained but it could break loose if the research lab isn't careful. At least one of these diseases has to have a weakness found, such as yearly vaccination for Cancer or AIDS. These are two well-known and dangerous diseases. In the future when the entire globe is explored, could new sicknesses be found?

Drugs. We've seen the movies and the signs and heard the lectures. People still don't get it though. Drugs are bad and they always will be. In 2020 a robot with special drug identifying sensors will have to be built. They would patrol the streets. I didn't say police officers because **sometimes** the police officers are addicted to that gunk anyway. An agreement will be made, the cop lets the guy go and he gets the drugs. Bad plan.

In the year 2020 we will not have all the comforts that we have now, nor will we have all the problems we have now. But if we can build a design for what we want the future to be like, then in time we can all have a bit of what we thought it would be like and appreciate it because it happened.

105

Grade 5 / 5ᵉ année
Hamilton-Wentworth
District School Board

Brian

A Journey to the Future

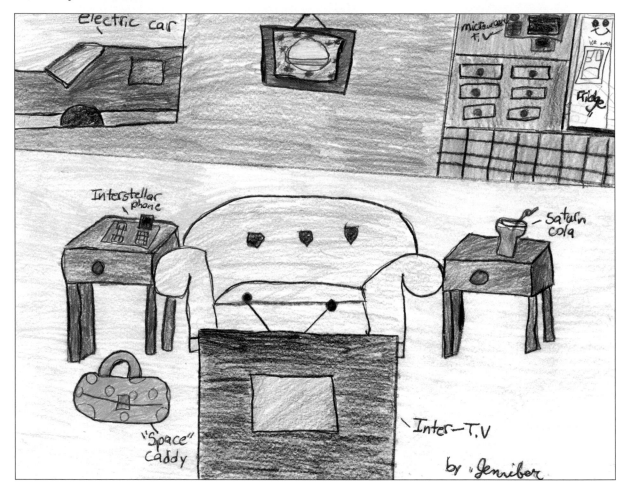

You are about to embark on a journey forward in time to the future of the year 2020. This is a place of electric cars and picture phones. I will be your tour guide, Jennifer. I have lived here for four years. I am from the 20th century so I will compare the things you have to the things I have here. The first place we will be visiting is the common person's house. We are now entering the person's house (blast of music). Which CD are we listening to? Could it be the Space Girls? Or could it be the Intergalactic Boys? Oh, I know what it is. It's the 100 Degrees.

Now into the living room we go. To your right are the sofa and the inter-TV. The inter-TV is a television with 2,020 channels. We add another channel every year.

Over there to your left is the interstellar-phone. This phone is a phone and remote control in one. If you want to talk on the phone you press the button labelled "Talk." If you want to use the TV you press the button labelled "Channel." If you want to use both you press the button labelled "Both." Also to make your conversation on the phone seem lifelike, we added a little TV so it seems you are actually talking face to face with that person. Right under the phone is the "Space" Caddy. The "Space" Caddy can hold anything you see (no matter what the size or the shape is). You could even fit an electric car in it!

Speaking of electric cars, I'm sure back in the 20th century you don't have these kinds of cars. These cars don't run on gasoline. They run on a battery. They go the same speed as gasoline cars. But you just have to charge the battery every 50 hours.

Now, on to the kitchen. The two appliances that really changed are the fridge and the microwave. The fridge can give you ice, water, and a friendly conversation while you wait. In the fridge there is a nice refreshing drink called Saturn Cola. This is a special kind of cola. This cola has a 50 sunblock in it so when you go outside you don't have to put any kind of sunblock on. The microwave has a 10-inch TV installed in it so you can catch up on your soaps while you wait for your snack to heat. This concludes our tour. Goodbye and happy travelling!

107

Grade 6 / 6ᵉ année
Dufferin-Peel Catholic
District School Board

Jennifer

La naissance de l'Ontario

Moi je vois l'Ontario
Avec des robots et des autos
Des animaux
Comme ils sont beaux
Ils seront encore plus beaux
Quand ils voleront en haut
De l'Ontario
Nous pourrons voir
L'Ontario longtemps
En respirant
L'air pur de l'Ontario
Comme ce sera beau

Pour que tout ça arrive
Je vais recycler pour que les scientistes
aient de nouveaux matériaux pour construire
de nouvelles inventions
Moi je vais demander à tous les gens
de la terre, de mettre des sacs volants sur
les animaux et ainsi de faire la nouvelle
naissance de l'Ontario

Jacob Lafrance

5ᵉ année / Grade 5
Conseil scolaire du district
catholique de l'Est Ontarien

Giant Steps to 2020

Just imagine learning about Christopher Columbus through the eyes of Virtual Reality headgear. Each student is seated in a cosmic-shaped desk with their own personal computer, experiencing crossing the Atlantic Ocean with the crew of the Santa Maria and reaching the New World of North America. I think this will be the way of learning in the year 2020. In the year 2020 I will be 33 years old. At the new schools I think there will be a drinking fountain that will ask what your preference will be like pop, water, juice, or milk.

The new popular place for vacationing will be on the moon. Imagine a March break on the moon, catching a few moonbeams. Sounds just out of this world. Also, there will probably be robots that will do chores for you so you can relax and have fun.

There will be a new popular type of cruise control in your car so you can relax your legs, and it will also steer your car to your destination. All you need to do is program it before you leave your home.

Clothing will be made of natural fibres that are biodegradable and will be recycled at your local shopping mall. To those people who lead busy lifestyles; they will be able to fax their food order from their car so it can be ready at the take-out window when they arrive. This will be terrific for me since I will be leading quite a busy lifestyle of my own. I will be driving around in my Chevrolet truck. While driving, I will take in messages from my electronic secretary. I will strive to be the best criminal lawyer that Brantford has ever seen. I will try to solve all the difficult criminal cases in the city of Brantford. As far as the March break is concerned, I think I'll just spend it on the moon, and take advantage of that "one giant step for mankind."

Michael King

Grade 7 / 7ᵉ année
Brandt-Haldimand-Norfolk Catholic
District School Board

109

110

L'Ontario dans l'an 2020

Introduction
Bonjour, je m'appelle Kristen Provost et je voudrais vous faire part de certains reportages de l'an 2020. Vous savez que chaque jour la technologie s'améliore de plus en plus vite, et ceci veut dire que dans l'an 2020 nous aurons de nouveaux éléments.

La médecine de l'Ontario
Si nous allons sur le côté médecine, il y aura sûrement de grandes améliorations sur la technologie du coeur, du crâne, des poumons, etc... et l'homme vivra encore plus longtemps.
    Aussi, c'est à espérer que l'on pourra prévenir les maladies.

Le téléphone de l'Ontario
Comme vous le savez, avec le téléphone indicatif d'aujourd'hui
nous pouvons voir qui nous a téléphoné. Nous pouvons également
voir leur numéro de téléphone afin de les rappeler. Donc, le
téléphone de l'an 2020 nous démontrera peut-être la personne
même sur un écran. Mais encore là, il y aura certaines restrictions.

Le marché monétaire de l'Ontario
Aussi, sur le marché monétaire, plus personne n'aura de l'argent comptant dans leur poche. Il y aura une nouvelle carte passe-partout qui indiquera l'endroit où l'argent sortira, ou encore, si tu veux le mettre sur une carte de crédit. Une seule carte au lieu de 25!

La nature de l'Ontario
Vers l'an 2020, la nature de l'Ontario va beaucoup changer.
Nous aurons de nouvelles fleurs qui ont du pollen rose. Ces fleurs
s'appelleront: Les Roses Jardin. Également, nous pourrons en faire
pousser. Il faudrait surtout qu'il pleuve pour que ça pousse.
Ce sera aussi un médicament contre le cancer.

Conclusion

Ceci termine mon projet sur l'Ontario. Et c'est certain que j'essaierai d'apprendre davantage sur la technologie et connaître de nouvelles inventions. Alors, merci d'avoir écouté et lu mon projet de l'Ontario dans l'an 2020. Si vous tournez la page, vous allez voir l'Ontario quand va arriver l'an 2020, il y aura beaucoup de changements! Au revoir et prêtez un regard sur l'Ontario en l'an 2020.

114

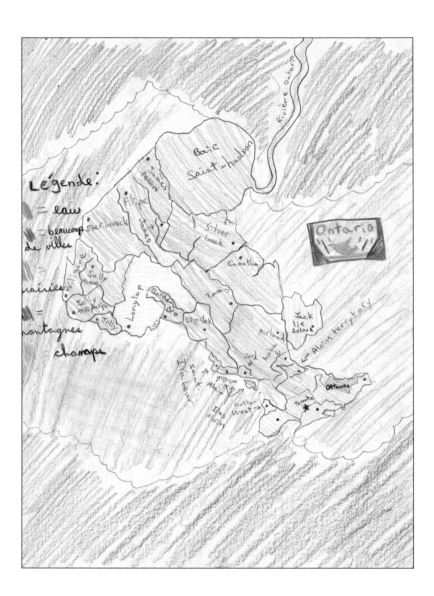

Kristen Provost

4e année / Grade 4
Conseil scolaire du district catholique
de l'Est Ontarien

Curing Diseases

In the year 2020 I will be 28 year old. I plan to make Ontario hospitals better by having medecine that can cure diseases like cystis fibrosis cancer and other diseases that we can not cure yet.

Grade 2 / 2ᵉ année
Toronto District School Board

Caitlyn Wilson

21st Century Creations

In the twenty-first century when you want to play basketball or soccer and the ball is flat, what do you do? You can get a ball that when it gets flat it pumps itself up again. You can have a special liquid that seeps into the ball. The liquid pumps it back up for you. You could have a special valve which allows the ball to inflate when you bounce it fast. You can put the ball in the sun. It has to get above 40°C. You could put the ball in cold water. It has a chemical reaction.

Benjamin Frizell

In the 21st century, you would give them blankets, pillows, shoes, clothes and food because they have no food. I want to give them jobs so they can buy their own things. You can collect the stuff from people who do not want it.

Tammy Arnold

In the 21st century, I would make a machine that would clean the air. The bad air turns into fresh air. I would put it by factories on smokestacks. It would make less pollution. It would stop a lot of people from getting sick.

Devin McGrath

In the 21st century I want to invent a pill that would increase your life span. Every time people take one they live five more years. It tastes like cookies and cream chocolate bars. It does not cost a lot of money. It is a really small pill. It is bright orange so if you drop it you can find it. It does stop the aging process. So if you are 85 when you take it, when you are 90, you will still look 85. When you are at the age of 65, you can take it if you want to. In each bottle there are one hundred pills. You have to see a doctor to get a prescription.

Cody Kevin King

In the 21st century I am going to build a building where war weapons go after the war. There is going to be underground helicopter parking with new and improved security systems and tubes that take you all over the building. All the rooms would be the same size. There's the electrical room, and the suit room, and the jail.

Adam Timmons

Class Project
Projet de classe

Grades 4 & 5 / 4e et 5e année

In the 21st century I am going to design a car that can drive on land, ride in water, and fly in the air. The fuel in the gas tank is non-polluting to the air or water. To make the car ride in water or in the air it has a propeller with a pipe attached to the engine to make it run. In the water the car goes just as fast as it does on ground. And in the air the car goes (4x) four times faster than on ground. On the ground the vehicle goes as fast as a regular car. The car is called a 3 Type B.R.M.P.

Bryce Patry

In the 21st century I am going to invent a robot that can operate by itself or by virtual reality control. This robot will do anything you want it to. It will also know how to make artificial limbs for animals. To tell you more, a virtual reality control is something like a visor: you put it around your eyes to control the robot. It would know how to do things from someone who knows how. It would also know how to make artificial animal limbs by the programmer.

Matt Cleary

117

I would like to invent a chute for transportation in the 21st century. There are some buttons on the side that have names of countries, towns, cities and so on. It goes faster than cars and it is safer than cars or planes. You step in the door and it sucks you up and you fly to the place you want to go. It flies through the air and if you want to go across the sea it goes over the sea. And that is what I want to invent in the 21st century.

S. Napier

In the 21st century I want to invent a computer built into a desk. The computer would be like a laptop. You would just need a notebook. You can write everything in it. The computer wires will be built in the desk. You can write essays on it. You will save it on your disk and print on a different computer that has a printer on it. There are only five computers in a class. And five people are hooked into one printer. And when you open your computer there is a button. You press it and it pops out of your desk. And that is what I want to invent in the 21st century.

Bridget Manahan

In the 21st century, I would like to invent a dog and cat leash. It looks like a round Frisbee, with lights and four legs with wheels. If the leash needed to stop, he could put down his brakes. The leash runs by battery. If your dog or cat tries to run off, there will be a voice that says, "No boy (or girl), stay," and that's what I would like to invent.

Amara J. McVeety

118

In the 21st century I would like to invent a wheelchair that will allow people to reach things they could not reach before. Hit a button and two cylinders push you up. Push it again and you come down. Push a lever and move forward, pull it back and move backward, move it left or right and turn.

Duncan MacKenzie

In the 21st century I want to invent a book for blind people. It works by pressing a button and it will tell the story. It looks like a normal book but with buttons on it. It will be a medium sized book. It will not cost a lot. It doesn't need charging at all, because it charges by itself.

Sarah Dugdale

In the 21st century I would like to invent a pill for diabetic people. If they take the diabetic pill, they would be able to eat as much as they want to pay for. Or as they can afford. I'm writing this My Ontario sheet because I have a nice boy in my class who is a diabetic. He got diagnosed the day after Halloween.

Cody Frizell

In the 21st century I would like to make a penknife for when you go camping. Not for school, because it will slice. It will open other things. It will be handy and easy to carry and if you get lost you can start a fire or make marks so people can find you and help you.

Todd Thomson

In the 21st century I am going to invent shoes that can make disabled people who have foot problems walk. The reason why I want to invent a pair of shoes like this is because I feel bad for the people who can't walk or run. I bet they would be happy when they heard about them. They would be operated by having four wheels on each shoe. The wheels would move 30 centimetres, brake, roll, and stop.

John Trafford

Class Project
Projet de classe

Grades 4 & 5 / 4ᵉ & 5ᵉ année

In 21st century I would like to be part of a group that makes a visor for blind people. You would hook it up to a computer and it would help you to see. You'd press a button on the top of the visor, then unplug the visor from the computer and you could see other things. Every hour you would have to hook it back up to the computer, then unplug the visor again. It would be called "the Visor of Hope." If you wanted one, it would be in a hospital, and nursing lounges. It would be affordable.

Elizabeth Carter

In the 21st century, I would like to help design a car radio with four sets of headphones for four people to listen to four individual favourite tunes. A remote for people in the back seat to use with buttons for four stereos,1234 on/off (the headphones) and 5 (the grand stereo), play, stop, ff., rwd (for tape deck and CD player), vol. (for tape, CD and tuner), AM/FM, up down (tuner). Even better, to help save the battery, the stereos will shut themselves off, if the stereos have been untouched for one hour or the car is shut off.

August Jahn-Matysiak

In the 21st century what I would like to invent would be a robot that would do all my chores for me. I would call it Mellybot after me. I could sell it in stores. Everybody would have a robot to do their chores. It would be cool! It wouldn't cost a lot. You could recharge it by plugging the battery in the recharger at night. Kids would have more free time and time to do homework.

Melanie Elizabeth Fisher

119

In the 21st century I'm going to make a plane that can be a house and can be a plane. There is one rule just because it doesn't need gas. Well, when it's a house you have to charge the battery. It can hold 500 people. It can even have a stove, toilet, bathtub, and a TV room.

Mike Varcoe Rediker

My human-made robot is good at stuff or at everything, actually. It can get you stuff, make stuff, clean up for you, and help you that way. It is good doing play stuff with you. There would be 10 in each house, and in an apartment, 15. So it is a good thing that there are a lot of robots in space and in the world today.

Joseph Hall

120

For the 21st century I want to invent a cure for cancer. I'm going to make the cure so it tastes good and in many different flavours. It won't make people sick. People will actually want to take their medicine and I'll make it so they only have to have two teaspoons and wait about a day and their cancer will be gone. For the 21st century I think that sounds good.
Angela Bedford

For 21st century, I would like to invent a clock that when you clap it twice, it tells you what time it is. This clock will help people to not be late for work. It will tell blind people what time it is too. This clock will be affordable too. I want to invent this because I feel I need to do something for people who are blind.
Anna Kravacek

What I would like to invent in the 21st century is a bathing suit that would make you swim faster. I would do this by sewing the material all in straight lines to let the water flow over you and tight to your body. So the looseness would not slow you down. This will decrease your time and change the world record. This bathing suit will also come in all different colours.
Lorie Strutz

I would like to invent a pen that if you don't know how to write, you can tell it to write for you. Just put your hand on the pen and tell it what to do.
Rhys Orme

In the 21st century, I would like to invent goalie pads that when you go down they inflate. Some goalies have bad knees and the pads would protect them. The pads would have zippers to replace the inflated protective materials. After every game the goalie would zip out the recycled materials and replace them. They are not that much money.
Justin Moore

In the 21st century I am going to invent a money tree. (How to grow it) The way you grow it is you get a seed and you cut it open and you put money in it and wait five years and cut the money off. (How to keep the money on) The way you keep the money on it is to put an electric fence around it. (How to take the money off) You take the money off by cutting it off.
Dustin McMunn

**Class Project
Projet de classe**

Grades 4 & 5 / 4ᵉ & 5ᵉ année

Four Psychologists and Technology

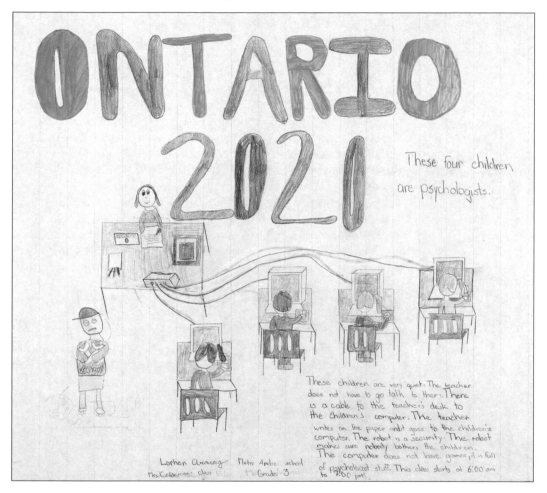

These children are very quiet. The teacher does not have to go talk to them. There is a cable from the teacher's desk to the children's computers. The teacher writes on the paper and it goes to the children's computers. The robot is a security guard. The robot makes sure nobody bothers the children. The computer does not have games, it is full of psychologist stuff. This class starts at 6:00 a.m. to 7:00 p.m.

Grade 3 / 3e année
Dufferin-Peel Catholic
District School Board

Lorhen Arauag

122

The Biggest Change? Technology!

This is my perception of Ontario will be like in
the year 2020:

By the year 2020 technology will bring the biggest change in
Ontario. The thing that is constantly changing, even now, is the
computer. By the year 2020 computers will still exist, but not as we
know them now. Talking computers do exist, but in twenty-one years
they will be the norm. The keyboard will not be needed. The monitor
will be interchangeable with the TV screen. We will do everything
through the computer: shop for groceries, pay our bills, buy cars, buy
houses, read books, make supper and much, much more.

The telephone will be able to do some amazing things, such as
translate. If you are speaking to someone in Japan who doesn't
know English and you don't know Japanese, you can have a
conversation. You will also be able to see the person you are
talking to. The telephone will most likely be part of the computer.

The television will become extreme. It will be like a mini indoor
theatre. The sound will be incredible. It will feel like you are part
of the movie, not just watching it.

Cars will change in a positive way. Cars create a lot of pollution
and people will want a change. Someone will come up with a non-
pollution car motor. It would have to be something simple, not an
electric motor because they are too much of a hassle to keep
recharging. Wouldn't it be something if a car could run on water?
It wouldn't cost anything to refuel and it is great for the
environment. Eventually cars will look more like round flying
saucers, and the sky will become a huge highway. This won't
happen for quite a while, certainly not by the year 2020.

There will be a new wave of building designs with totally new
shapes and structures. Houses, office buildings, and stores will
completely change. It will take next to no time to put up a
building. The inside will probably not change by much. It will
probably be quite similar to the houses of today. We will have a

few more gadgets to play with in the house. Appliances will be more efficient. Some examples would be vacuum cleaners vacuuming on their own, ovens baking things in half the time they do now. The dishwasher will go a little further by putting away the dishes. There will also be a new invention that will iron and fold clothes. I think I might even come up with this invention. My mother would love me for it.

Other than technology, I think schools will change the most in the year 2020. I still believe that robots will not replace teachers as most people would suspect. I just think that teachers will have a lot more utilities for their use than they do now. They will have a big, flat screen instead of a blackboard at the front of the room. The screen would be very useful because in some way it would be like a television except it would be used for educational purposes. By then all the schools will have colour photocopiers. Every student will have their own personal computer at their desk. That would mean that the desks would have to be larger. School would become fun all the time, not sometime.

You have just read my view of the future. In general life will be much easier than it is now, just like it is much easier now-a-days than it was twenty-one years ago. It will be more difficult to find jobs because of the technology. Machines will be doing a lot of the work that man does today. Hopefully, we can find work where machines cannot take over. It may or may not turn out the way I think it will, but whatever the future is, I hope it will be a good one.

Grade 7 / 7e année
Hamilton-Wentworth
District School Board

John Vrakela

New Inventions Will Be Created

I think that Ontario will be very different in the year 2020. First, I think that there will be a glass dome around Ontario to protect us from the pollution and UV rays. Also, I think that people will be lazy in the year 2020 so I think that elevators will have replaced stairs because everyone will be too out of shape to climb them; sidewalks will become moving conveyors and most people will do their shopping on the home shopping network.

There will probably be a space station not far from Earth and a base on the moon that you can visit. You will also be able to visit some of the planets in our solar system too because scientists will have invented warp speed.

I think the buildings in Ontario will be very different from today's buildings in that the structures will be more interesting to look at. In some of the factories, I think that robots will be doing the work that some of us do today.

I think that our transportation will be different too. A lot of people will ride around on hover boards and the cars that the people will drive will be powered by garbage (that will keep all of the garbage dumps from filling up).

I think that new inventions will be created like the hologram projector, the replicator and a new species of animal will be discovered in the Amazon and will become a common domestic pet.

So that is what I think Ontario will look like in the year 2020.

125

Grade 7 / 7ᵉ année

Ashley Cooper
Julia Foote

126

2020—A Journey through Time

Within the Mega City, formally known as Toronto, lived a scientist by the man of Eric. Eric worked busily in his basement, not seeing the light of day. All this hard work was done so he could accomplish his dream. A dream to view how humanity will progress, to see how his own children would prosper. For years he worked to make a perfect time machine. Finally, on April 21, 1999, Eric's dream came true, he had developed the world's first time machine.

He was unsure whether it worked. He knew there was only one way to find out, unfortunately this meant risking his own life since the slightest error could cause every cell in his body to evaporate. Eric had to follow his dream. Eric decided to follow through his plan. He began pushing buttons, pulling levers, and then came the moment of truth, the door opened....Eric had a good feeling about this. He walked inside and pulled a handlebar which activated the time machine. Every cell in his body evaporated and then began moving faster than the speed of time. His cells then began to re-form into his body when he reached his destination in the future. Eric stepped out of the time machine and observed his surroundings, he was baffled. Eric approached a nearby shopkeeper and casually inquired where he was and what was the year? The shopkeeper stared at him in disbelief as if he believed Eric was insane. To Eric's surprise the shopkeeper began yelling for help. Eric froze, he was beginning to regret facing the future, when he noticed something in the corner of his eye, a huge complex with an enormous video screen on the side of it, which exclaimed the word "futuristic." He wondered what that meant. Suddenly two robots approached him, they were carrying some kind of laser device. The machine made loud, high pitch noises. The robots seemed to be talking to each other. Eric approached the robots and tried to communicate. To his surprise the robots spoke English. They explained that they were part of the Mega City's new line of defense. Eric asked the robots who was the main city's historian. The robots replied that there was no historian but there was a city data bank, which can be accessed through the Internet. Eric explored the region a little more and was shocked when he realized there was no sign of nature. Eric had many unanswered questions, so he found a computer and accessed the city data bank. To Eric's horror he learned that the planet had been destroyed five years earlier in the year 2015. This was due to world conflict, power struggles, human greed and pollution. Eric learned that after the war the world was rebuilt. Unfortunately, though humans had accomplished a lot, they were not able to recreate nature. The world was a mass of steel, concrete and other synthetic materials. Eric was left disgusted, he realized that technology and human accomplishment was good, but not at the expense of nature, which could not be compromised. Eric headed back to his time, where he belonged. He took a long walk through his neighbourhood park and he realized how lucky he was. Eric had a new mission in life — he was going to preserve nature. He did not want the world to become a cold world. He had to ensure that his children would enjoy the same luxuries of seeing trees, hearing birds chirping, smelling fresh air....Eric is presently in his basement working on accomplishing his new goals — for a better future for the next generation.

Grade 5 / 5ᵉ année
Toronto District School Board

Rohan Kebar

128

A Dream about the Future!

SLAM. I had just got home from a tough day at school and nothing could happen to cheer me up. It was a Wednesday afternoon and the sun was shining warmly, the birds were chirping happily and the black TV in the old living room was just screaming silently, "Watch me, watch me." But, as usual, our English teacher occupied us with another assignment that had to be done the following day. Our topic was "Ontario in the year 2020." I could even remember those exact words, "think positive," coming out of my teacher's mouth. "What could possibly be so great about growing up?" I asked myself. Nothing, was the first thing that came to mind. I already hated the fact that I was growing up and everything that my life revolved around seemed to be getting harder. I could just predict what was going to happen in the future. I'd be in school, carrying a load of books in my hand, needing to wear masks over our heads to keep us alive from the pollution, and the place would be way overcrowded. Time had passed and when the sun finally set that evening, I had still been locked up in my room growling about this assignment. As I took out a sheet of paper and picked up my pen, I fell fast asleep on my desk.

Rise and Shine, Rise and Shine. Something was poking me and making funny noises. *Rise and Shine, Rise and Shine.* There it was again but louder! I leaned over and barely opened my eyes, and right before me was a robot poking me on the shoulder and repeating the same phrase over and over again. In less than a second, I shot out of bed staring at the robot with amazement. I slowly crept towards the large moving piece of metal and looked at its stomach. It had been operated by computer and on the screen it read, *"Are you awake yet? Press YES or NO."* I pressed *YES* and the machine stopped talking and just stood there as still as a rock. It was probably another one of those old pranks that my dorky 15-year-old brother was trying to do. Just to make sure he didn't do anything else, I looked around the room and scanned everything carefully. Nothing had been touched or moved. So I walked quietly over to my brother's room and yelled with great anger, "Ha, ha, funny joke. Now get that foolish robot out of my room!" He looked at me with his somewhat innocent puppy eyes and said, "I swear on my life that I didn't do anything." I just stomped out of his room and went back to mine. I went to open my closet and the computer on my desk started making tiny noises. As I walked over, the only thing on my computer was a blank square requesting me to type up what I wanted to wear. "Okay, this is odd," I whispered to myself. I wrote in "Flared Khakis, black tank top, white socks." Then pressed ENTER and after 15 seconds, the screen read, "It is now OK to open your closet door." As I opened the door, to my surprise, the outfit that I asked for appeared right before me. "Remarkable!" I yelled. "Whatever is going on, I couldn't care less because I like this." I quickly put on my clothes and rushed downstairs for breakfast.

My mother and father were sitting by the kitchen table sipping coffee and reading a really small laptop that was the size of a calculator. "Umm...mother, father what are you doing?" I asked in a quivery yet confused voice. "Reading the newspaper," was their only response. I gave them a weird look and tried to ignore that remark. When I walked towards the refrigerator, on the big, white door was another computer! "Gee, why are there so many computers in the house?" I mumbled. But this one was a menu. My options to press were: *breakfast, lunch or dinner*. Without even thinking, I pressed my small finger against the screen for breakfast. A list of morning foods showed up. I pressed any of the items I wanted, and as I opened the door, the food appeared before my eyes. "This is incredible!" I shrieked. But even though everything was turning out more than perfect, I needed to know what was going on. I mean, this incredible invention of having computers do everything was freaking me out. While eating my cereal, I decided that as soon as I got to school, I was going to find out what was going on by looking it up on the Internet. When I finished my delicious breakfast, I headed for the door. "Sweetheart," uttered my mother, "where are you going?" "School, remember the place that I go to learn things?" I said suspiciously. "Nice try honey, go right up to your room and start your program." So that's what I did. I marched right upstairs and went towards my computer. I was determined to go surf the Net and find out what was happening but as I logged on, it read:

Wednesday May 9th, 2020
9:00 a.m.   Math: www.math.grade8.com
10:00 a.m. English: www.english.grade8.com
11:00 a.m. French: www.french.grade8.com
12:00 p.m. LUNCH BREAK
1:00 p.m.   Physical Education:
            www.physed.grade8.com: learning
            push ups.
2:00 p.m.   Social Science:
            www.socsci.grade8.com
3:00 p.m.   Science: www.science.grade8.com
4:00 p.m.   end of classes
Remember: Your room door is now locked
            until lunch.

The very first thing that caught my attention was the year 2020. "I'm in the year 2020!?!" I yelped across the room and I couldn't believe my eyes. I looked at the bottom of the screen

and it was 15 minutes until I had to get to work. I tried opening the door but I was locked, so I decided to call one of my friends. I looked around the room for my phone but it wasn't there. When I got back to the computer, one of the icons was labeled as "my numbers." I double-clicked it and a column of my friends' numbers emerged. I clicked the name Lisa, who was my best friend, and then a screen appeared with her face on it. "Hey!" yelled Lisa. "Why are you on my computer screen?" I said in a daze. "What do you mean, silly? How else could we talk?" Just then I remembered that I was in the future. I remembered hearing that one day I would be able to talk to a person over a computer and be able to see their face, but that time, I didn't believe it. "So this is what it's like in the future," I snickered with a grin on my face. "Not bad." I finished talking to Lisa and went to my sites for my work. My first subject was math. As I got into the web site, my teacher (Mr. Smith) came up in a little box. Just like old times, he taught us a lesson and then sent each student he had homework over email. Each subject was the exact same routine. Lessons, then homework. At lunch, while eating a peanut butter and jelly sandwich, I surfed the Internet and looked up the subject "Timeline of Ontario." When I got into the site, I couldn't believe the incredible yet fantastic reconstruction of Ontario. My own province had improved so much that it even put goosebumps on my skin. Some of the unbelievable changes were things like the following headlines:

• Limit on population to avoid overcrowding
• School at home
• New Solar Cars
• Robot helpers and computers CAN run
  everything
• Cure for cancer

130

The best headline that I read was:

ONTARIO WAS VOTED "BEST PROVINCE IN ALL OF CANADA"

Though the changes were great, it was a drastic move!

The day seemed long but as time passed it eventually came to 4:00 pm. My bedroom door finally unlocked and the first place I wanted to go was outside. I was expecting a lot of pollution, but to my surprise, it was cleaner than ever. The grass was almost emerald green, the street had not even a single piece of garbage and the air smelt like fresh flowers. I also noticed that each house had three recycling bins and everybody looked really healthy. As I crept towards the road, a weird looking car drove by. That must be the new solar energized cars. No wonder everything is clean, I thought to myself.

Later that evening, when I finished dinner at around 8:00 pm, I walked up to my room again and lay still on my bed. I stared at the ceiling and thought about how completely PERFECT my day was. In less than a second, I fell fast asleep with a wide smile on my face.

Kathy! *Kathy!* I woke up with someone nudging me on my shoulder. I took one blink and my eyes were wide awake. My brother was standing there laughing hysterically at me and replied, "You fell asleep, kid." It was all a dream. Was it possible that something so perfect ended up as a dream? I looked on my table and knew exactly what to write for my assignment.

I started it off like this: "The Best is to come out of Ontario…"

Kathy Chiu

Grade 8 / 8e année
Toronto District School Board

Vignettes par Morgan

Je vais dire de mon rêve. Dans mon rêve je suis dans mon auto et dans mon auto j'ai une toilette. Dans mon rêve, mon auto vole comme un oiseau et va vite comme un avion. Une fois arrivée à ma maison qui est faite en plastique, je demande pour quelque chose à manger. Les machines me donnent un hamburger, des frites, et du jus. Ma nourriture est en vitamines. Le soir est venu et j'allume les lumières qui sont des toiles d'araignées. Je m'assois sur ma chaise et je lis mon livre. Mon robot fait le ménage. Je vais à mon ordinateur et je lui dit qu'il me faut de la nourriture dans la maison, mon ordinateur pense pour moi et commande ma nourriture. Dans l'Ontario 2000 il n'y a plus de magasins. Avant que je me couche mes deux chiens font des trucs magiques. C'est le temps d'aller me coucher, je mets mes lunettes noires pour me faire dormir. Bonne nuit!

131

3e année / Grade 3
Conseil scolaire du district des écoles
catholiques du Sud-Ouest de l'Ontario

Morgan Bradley

132

The Future World of Transportation and Communications

This is my guide to the future in the year 2020. Imagine a smarter, safer and more technologically advanced world. No fast vehicles zooming around town in danger of hitting children. Imagine being able to drive as high as an airplane and to be able to listen to any music you wish to without paying more than once. Imagine seeing the other person that you are talking to on the phone even if you are in different countries, or not having to walk downtown but to have the sidewalks do the walking for you. Well, soon you can stop imagining because all of this will happen! There is only a small matter of time until everyone's lives will become safer, healthier, less expensive and practically unbelievable.

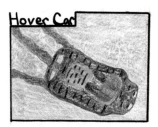

Hover Cars

These high-tech vehicles are shaped like Ferraris and come in any colour. They do not move on land for they have no wheels. Instead they use extremely powerful air jets on their bottom, front, and backs to shoot them through the air in any direction and up to 600km/h. They are automatically sensored so that they do not touch each other, buildings or even skyscrapers. To land, you push a button and it lands for you on its bumpercar-type bottom. They are all equipped to fit six people inside. The Hover Bus is exactly the same, except that it is extended to fit sixty people inside.

Bubble Ships

Instead of Toronto's streets being filled with taxicabs, its sky, along with skies everywhere, will be swarming with these interesting looking two-seater vehicles that resemble your everyday fictitious alien spaceships. They have a see-through glass dome over them and a wing on each side that measures about one and a half metres long and 60 centimetres in width. They run on very high-powered air jets that let you go up to 650 km/h, making sure that you reach your destination on time. They are also sensored not to hit each other or buildings. To land Bubble Ships, push the button that will release a large pair of suction cups. They are attached to the Bubble Ship by ropes. These ropes are used to reel the Bubble Ship in until you are safely landed. Bubble Planes are the same as Bubble Ships except that they are larger and can hold more people.

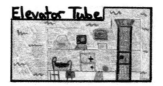

Elevator Tubes

Don't use stairs or those slow elevators that require buttons to be pushed, simply tell the Elevator Tube what level you want, and you're there. These tubes come in any sizes and heights, from two-level houses up to even the CN Tower's height. All you have to do is step inside the doorway onto the platform, tell the voice box what level you want and you are instantly pushed up the tube. The air pressure inside the tube pushing against you in every direction stops you from getting hurt or even messy hair.

Moving Sidewalks

Tired of walking? Just step on one of these conveyor belt escalators and it does the walking for you. They will cover most of the entire city. To turn, just wait until the next intersection, then stomp your foot on the side that you would like to turn on. Stepping off is just a matter of taking a step. The sides are softly cushioned just in case you fall.

C.P.H.'s

Children's Personal Hovercrafts are extremely sharp looking and extremely fast. They can reach a speed of 110 km/h while hovering 30 cm off the ground, making sure that young drivers do not get scared of slipping out of their seatbelts. They are designed like today's 3 wheel tricycles for toddlers except that they are much bigger and do not have wheels. Instead, they have suction cups on their bottoms that are used to land, and when the air from inside the cups is forced against the ground it causes it to lift. Handlebars are used to turn in any direction you wish. To land, just push the red button by your foot. C.P.H.'s are individually fingerprint X-rayed when purchased. When you first sit down on

your C.P.H., insert your finger into the hole in between the handlebars. If the machine recognizes your fingerprint, it will automatically start up the jet-powered suction cups for you.

Jetpacks

These small air jet devices are easy to use. By just flicking the switch on your jetpack's belt, you are shot up into the air, although not too high for those who are afraid of heights. They will hover around one metre in the air and travel up to 50 km/h. They are run by solar power. They do not use exhaust that pollutes the air, so they are much healthier.

Telescreens

Is your finger tired from dialing those phone numbers? You can stop this by buying one of these high-tech, low priced, fascinating and extraordinary machines. They will replace computers, telephones and cellular phones. For your convenience they are voice activated. To get into any computer program or the Internet, just tell the machine and it instantly shows up on the screen. To type essays, just read the words and they appear on the screen. To phone anyone, just say their first and last name and it instantly shows up on the screen. To type essays, just read the words and they appear on the screen. To phone anyone, just say their first and last name and it instantly shows a list of all the people who have the name that you said. This is when you tell it which number on the list it is and your machine and the receiver's machine will be connected. When they arrive at their telescreen you will be able to see them on your screen and they'll be able to see you on their screen. While you talk they can hear you and see you talking, just as if you were in the same room as them. The screens are minimized into little watches worn around your wrist. For the Telewatch, you have to dial up the number by hand and punch in the small numbers on your watch.

133

134

Choose Box

Forget about putting CDs, cassette tapes in or even adjusting the dial to your favourite radio station, just buy a Choose Box. These very intelligent machines carry with them in memory every song ever made. You only have to tell the Choose Box what band or songs that you would like to hear and it plays it for you. Every house will have a short antenna on them making sure that every new song that comes out is quickly downloaded into your Choose Box.

3D Holograph Projector

Instead of watching a 2D TV show or movie on a traditional television set, just click your remote control at your 3D Holograph Projector located on your ceiling and the actors will be life-sized and appear to be standing in your room. It will seem that you are right in the middle of the action. So don't take up space in your house with a television set, just install a 3D Holograph Projector into your ceiling and enjoy.

So as you now know, the year 2020 will be filled with new and advanced technical vehicles, machines and many other projects. Our problems today will be reduced by the hundreds, such as: pollution, car accidents, high phone bills, slow-moving traffic jams, flat tires and stuck elevators. There are going to be solutions to all of these problems, along with many more.

I know that I would hate for all of this not to happen. The world would be such a better place if there were enough dedicated people to help keep these plans moving toward the future. That's why I am going to open my own business when I grow up and have a company that works on electronics and vehicles. My friends also feel the same way about helping out. So I am going to make sure that we all work together to make the world a safer, healthier and more enjoyable environment, by becoming mechanical and electronical partners. The year 2020 is not very far away, and I am looking forward to all of the exciting inventions that will make our lives better.

Michael Gilbert

Grade 6 / 6ᵉ année
Avon Maitland District School Board

The Medicine Cabinet of 2020

Our artistic intention or message is to make the viewer see and think that there will be many cures for diseases, especially in Ontario, in the year 2020. We also want the viewer to see and think that since it is so high-tech now, technology will be even more advanced in the future. As a result, doctors and medical scientists will have help from the technology and try their best to discover and produce vaccines and treatment for the diseases which we now consider fatal.

To create our area of emphasis we used a bold and outstanding colour to make it stand out and become noticeable. It's also the biggest object in the whole picture and it is placed in the middle of the page. By doing this, it will make the viewer's eyes not only stay on the focal point but travel around the whole picture.

The reason why we chose to show "the Medicine Cabinet of 2020" is because we are interested in going into the field of medicine when we get older. We also want to be one of the people to find the cures for diseases in the future.

135

Grade 8 / 8ᵉ année

Mandeep Bhamra
Tamara Lutchman

Quatre histoires provenant d'une classe de 1re année

136

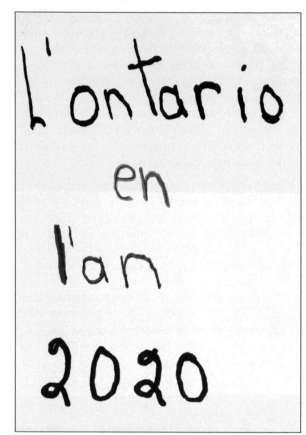

En l'an 2020 Je serai grand et grande comme Papa et Maman. L'ontario sera différent bien différent. Voici les changements qui auront lieu:

137

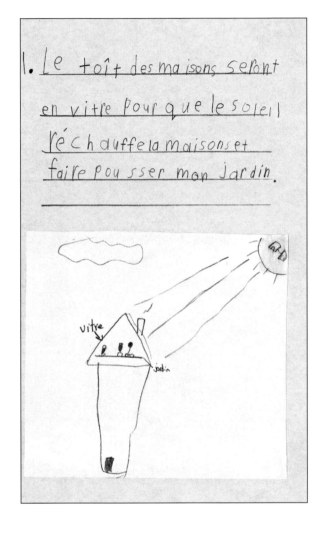

1. Le toît des maisons seront en vitre pour que le soleil réchauffe la maisons et faire pousser mon jardin.

2. Les autos vont avoir des couleurs différentes. Le jour les autos avanceront avec l'énergie du soleil et le soir la lumière des étoiles, et si il vente les autos iront plus vite.

138

3. Les robots vont nettoyer la maison couper le gazon, couper du bois et pelleter la neige.

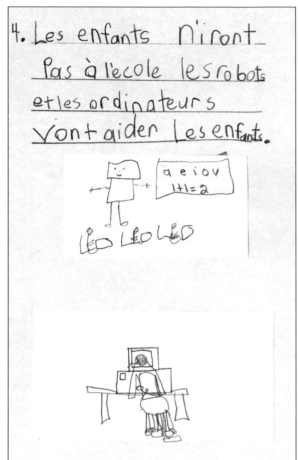

4. Les enfants n'iront pas à l'école les robots et les ordinateurs vont aider les enfants.

Brianne Lalande
Caroline
Christine Doiron
Dominik Gamache
George Bilodeau
Janique Jolbert
Jeffrey Turmelle
Joshua Lachance

Julie Massicotte
Mayer
Melanie Gauthier
Patrick Martel
Paul Emile Claueau
Serge Parent
Seth Walton
Sylvie Picotte
Tyler Gervais

1re année / Grade 1

In 2020 What Will It Be Like?

Okay, in the year 2020 I think that cars will be made into flying cars and you'll be able to fly anywhere in Canada. I also think that cars will be able to float in Canada, so if you have to go across lakes, you can float across.

Here is an example of the cars.

Now let's talk about what the house will look like. Some of the homes will become tree houses and the others will be tall buildings with rings in the year 2020. I'm not so sure what your house will be like, but I hope that my house will be tall with rings. Like this (one shown).

Cool, did I just hear that in the year 2020 if you're starting school then it's free, no cost. You have to go to school for four days a week from 8:40 a.m. until 1:00 p.m. You'll have six to seven classes a day and you don't pick. I get to pick them for you. The schools will be bigger.

This is so funny but it might be true. Dogs, cats and all other kinds of animals can fly. Ha, you don't have to believe it but I do. Just think, dogs, cats and all the other animals flying around. That would be so cool. Oh, keep your eyes open, you might see a cow jump over the moon.

Now jobs. Let's see, jobs would be the same but you would get paid more than you do now because the world would have more money. So if you're a garbage man you would get paid more.

Now let's talk about some Gameboys and phones. Well, in the year 2020 there will be phones that you can watch TV on and you can play games and if you call someone, you can see them talking to you. COOL!!

Okay, here is a computer that you can put in your pocket and off you go.

Ashley MacKenzie

Grade 6 / 6e année

139

Journal of My Visit to 2020

My name is Erica Leigh. I am a reporter who has dropped into the year 2020 from 1999. The following is the journal of my short visit.

August 31st, or should I say 243-2020 (the 243rd day of the year 2020)

This is a different world. I am overwhelmed by the differences. I started out my day at the government's office, or more correctly, the *Authority's* HQ. I was issued a microchip, called a CHIP. It is a combination health card, driver's license, debit card and identification. I politely but firmly declined the preferred option of having this CHIP embedded under my skin, and I opted for having it on a wristband that cannot be removed. I immediately found this an astoundingly good idea. I mean, back in 1999, you have, like, 15 cards to keep track of, and if you lose one, you're toast. Just think of all the fraud you avoid and the time you save. I can't believe no one thought of this before. The only scary thing is, you can be tracked down anywhere, anytime, by the *Authority*. Oh well, just going with the flow. All good things have a bad side too.

Next stop, the pharmacy. I cannot begin to describe how much medicine has changed in the past 21 years. The single biggest difference is the doctors. Basically, there are none, besides a precious few specialists. At the pharmacy, you input your symptoms, temperature, and a drop of blood, etc., into a computer, and in a short time, the necessary pills are dispensed from a type of computerized vending machine. And the prick of the needle doesn't even hurt that much anymore. This is such a good idea, in that it will stop hundreds of misdiagnoses, errors, etc. This is such an improvement!

Oh yes, back to the reason for visiting the pharmacy. I need to buy my UNIPILL. This revolutionary pill contains all the necessary vitamins and minerals for my age and has something to smooth out your feelings and moods. It is not mandatory, but I think it is good. It stops so much of the anger that they think causes conflicts of personality and disagreements. They also believe that it is safer to be protected from our own feelings.

This took up most of my first day. And now I am retiring to my hotel. Everything is so sanitary. The sheets are made of soft, paperlike fibres. The bathroom and its contents are shrink-wrapped in plastic, with a new layer for every guest. Neat, eh? I think it's great! Goodnight.

246-2020

So much has happened in the past few days, it is unbelievable. It would take books to describe. So I'll just write about today. I had the opportunity to visit the school systems, or rather, ED1 through ED25. It is so computerized, it's unrecognizable. Not a scrap of paper in sight. Come to think of it, I haven't seen a single piece of paper since I arrived here. Anyways, even the kindergarten kids can type. Most of the classes do not have humans as teachers, which I think is great, because teachers can make mistakes and lose their temper. Instead, most are taught by interactive ED programs. I get no sense of sociality in these schools, no closeness of friends, no tension of enemies. This school seems to work surpisingly well, but it is all so cold-hearted. The pros outweigh the cons in this case, by a fair bit. But I am beginning to see how dangerous we humans can be if we are not controlled in some way.

This afternoon, I went for a walk in what is called the "indoor outdoors." The nature here is so full of the industrial pollution, allergens and other airborne particles. The *Authority* has created this indoor environment for people to come to. It resembles nature, but it is perfect. It is such a beautiful, calm, well-lit area, stretched over a few acres. This place seems really healthy. But in a small way, it doesn't feel quite real.

250-2020

It's been four days since I last had a spare moment to write. I've been thinking about the folk that actually live here. To be in this world all your life must be boring. I'm beginning to realize the magnitude of the trade-off between freedom and danger versus safety and the security of being controlled. Everything here is so anonymous, you could go a lifetime and no one would know your name, only your CHIP code. I think that's kind of sad.

251-2020

The only thing I could think of today was my feeling of imprisonment by this wristband CHIP. I can't shake the thought that someone is watching me, and could track my every move. Maybe I'm feeling paranoid, but I know the *Authority* could find me if they had the mind to. I am beginning to feel panicky. Very mild panic, of course, thanks to the UNIPILL, but panic nonetheless. Maybe I could talk to someone

about my concerns, but no one seems to have deep, meaningful talks anymore. This civilization is shallower, but I guess I'm not supposed to have deep things to talk about in the first place.

255-2020

I wished, for the first time in what feels like ages, that I could experience deep feelings, controlled by no one other than me. Not some insensitive, computer-crazed *Authority*, but me. Plain old me. I can still see how much safer it is to be controlled, and how dangerous humans would be left to their own devices in this excessively refined, civilized civilization. But I couldn't help wishing...

300-2020

The machine was wrong. Wrong, I tell you. The computer-controlled, allegedly infallible machine failed me. I had trusted that machines were perfect, and now that trust is shattered. But how can I complain to an insensitive pile of plastic and metal? I was right, I know I was right. Deep down in my heart. Do I even still have a heart? Yes, OK, just checking. I can't believe I've believed in this utter myth, this fragment of my imagination, for so long. Trusting a machine, created by humans, to be better than humans. I can't believe I took that controlling pill either. I've been brainwashed by technology. Yes, that's it, brainwashed by technology. Here, the motto is technology will save us, technology can rule us. I cannot find the words to express my feelings. At least I have feelings again. Not shallow sentiments, but true, deep, bona fide feelings. I feel incredibly lucky to have been

142

freed from the myth of technology. What an evil word. It nearly destroyed my life. My life. Yes, I still have a life. And I'm returning to really LIVE it. Live my life, complete with the uncontrolled people, the surprises life brings, the unexpected happenings and spontaneity. The danger, the exhilaration compared to here. I can't wait to be home again. Yes, back in archaic 1999. But what about the people still here? I feel like I'm the only one whose head is screwed on the right way. No one else here even wants to be saved. They have all forgotten what real life is about. Wait a minute. This is the future. This hasn't really happened yet. What can I do to keep our society from this spiralling, one-way path to destruction? Or utter sameness, with computer-controlled bodies and no souls. Every day, humans become more and more dependent on technology. It happens gradually, and we may not realize it. We are doomed, unless we learn, and learn in a hurry, to trust ourselves, to pay attention to our conscience, to take time out to relax, enjoy nature, friends and family. We have to value freedom, unconditional freedom. We have to believe in ourselves and in each other, not in machines, we need to trust each other. We have to take risks.

Jenny Alloway

Grade 9 / 9ᵉ année
Conseil scolaire du district
du Centre-Sud-Ouest

More Excitement in 2020

In the year 2020 I will be 31 years old. I would want all the cars to be computerized, so when you tell the car where to go, it would go there by itself. In the house there would be robots that would do everything for you. You won't have to cook, clean, or even read! The robots will do everything for you. Everybody will work 4 hours. The rest of the time the robots will work.

The sidewalks would move for you so you wouldn't have to walk. If you were riding your bike on the sidewalk, you would go faster than usual. There would also be a plane that could go underwater. It would be able to fly over a lake, then it would just crop into the water.

All the houses would be higher than now. The lowest one would be three floors. The highest would be seven floors. There would be an elevator that would take you to any floor. On the highest floor everybody would have a Jacuzzi and a pool.

There would be a (boys or girls) clothes spray, that if you sprayed it on yourself different clothes would appear on you. You can keep on switching till you like the clothes you have on. There would be a train called a Skytrain. It would take you to any main building in Ontario! It would have stops like a subway, so people can get in and out. I think Ontario would be more interesting and exciting in the year 2020 than it is now.

143

The House of 2020

144

Differences between houses in 2020 and houses today:

Aspect	Today	In 2020
Windows	Manually opening, can only Be one shade.	Shatter-proof, automatically Tinting, energy saving
Doors	Using a handle to open and Close them.	Automatically slides open when It detects motion. Germ free
Security	Security system with a key and passcode	Key, card, fingerprint, retina Scan, DNA test, passcode.
Food Preparation	Manually opening the fridge, And making a snack	Food is automatically made via a food replicator- voice orders
Energy	Electricity that you pay for.	All heated and powered by Solar panels.
Toilet	Disease-spreading plastic seats.	Heated stainless steel toilet (Automatically cleans itself)
Heat	Manual heat setting device.	Automatic temperature Adjustment.
Emergency Power	(None)	Water is collected from rain, And stored in the basement
Smoke & Pollution Filters	Smoke filter that hangs from Roof.	Filter outside house that keeps House 100% clean.
Transport to 2nd floor	Stairs that take physical work	Elevators that don't break down
Cleaning	Manual cleaning	Computerized automatic cleaning
Furniture	Bought furniture from store	The floor conforms to shape of desired furniture
Entertainment	Television, Radio, etc.	Holographic projection room
House Protection	Brick, wood, cement, etc.	Titanium to protect against storms
Closet	Manually picking out/storing Clothes	Automatically organizing closet
Sound	Radio, manually adjusting Volume, etc.	Voice-controlled speaker sys. Through house.

Other Aspects of The House of 2020:

- The house it on concrete stilts, to protect against landslides, mudslides, and floods.
- There is a water filtration system in the basement
- There is a vent on the main floor that takes the air in and sends it through filtration equipment in   the basement, to be re-circulated through the house.
- The house has rounded corners to make it look better, and for more support.

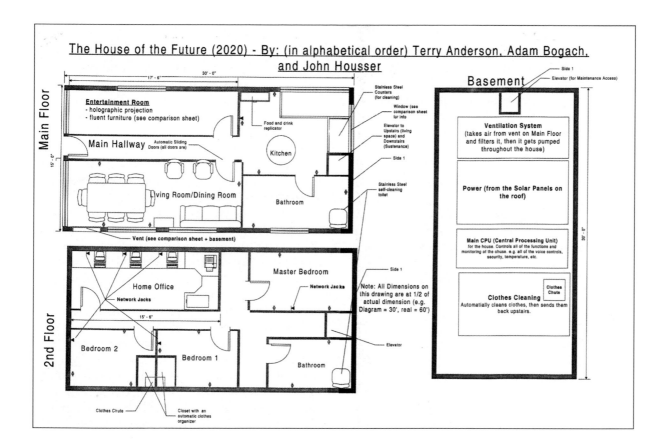

145

Grade 8 / 8e année
York Region District School Board

**Terry Anderson
Adam Bogach
John Housser**

MON ONTARIO

Les trous noirs

L'avenir nous réserve des surprises. De quoi aura l'air l'Ontario en 2020? Personnellement, j'ai mes propres théories et idées à propos de cela. Quelques idées vont peut-être sembler assez bizarres, mais laissez-moi vous les expliquer. Pour mieux imaginer l'Ontario de 2020, il faut qu'on examine les domaines qui évoluent rapidement comme les découvertes environnementales, technologiques et spatiales.

Je me demande ce que je ferai en 2020. Je crois que je deviendrai peut-être ingénieur. Pour améliorer l'économie du Canada et de l'Ontario, je développerai la technologie solaire pour produire de l'énergie qu'on pourra vendre aux autres pays. Vous vous demandez probablement comment je pourrai accomplir cette tâche. N'a-t-on pas déjà la technologie solaire? La réponse est assez simple. Je modifierai la technologie pour l'utiliser dans l'espace. Soutenu par le gouvernement canadien, on lancera une fusée, dirigée par des astronautes canadiens, dans l'espace, vers le soleil. Cette fusée sera équipée de panneaux solaires qui convertiront l'énergie du soleil en une énorme pile. La fusée sera motorisée par une technologie créée par la NASA, appelée une voile de vents solaires. Cette voile sera une voile spéciale qui pourra attraper les radiations émises par le soleil; ces radiations agiront comme un vent spécial qui poussera la voile et par conséquent, la fusée aussi. Ainsi, la fusée pourra s'approcher du soleil pour accumuler l'énergie nécessaire et convertir l'énergie dans une pile. Encore, les sceptiques demanderont : «Mais si on utilise les panneaux solaires sur terre, pourquoi est-ce qu'il faut les utiliser dans l'espace?» Sur terre, nous sommes protégés des rayons solaires UVC par la couche d'ozone. En théorie, ces types de rayons sont assez puissants. En envoyant la fusée au soleil, les rayons UVA, UVB et UVC pourront être accumulés à une intensité énorme. Après avoir fini de charger la pile spéciale, la fusée sera redirigée vers la terre où on pourra vendre l'énergie aux autres pays. Par conséquent, le Canada prospérera encore de ses ressources naturelles et l'économie de l'Ontario s'améliorera en créant de nouveaux emplois pour les gens canadiens. De cette façon, le Canada jouera un plus grand rôle sur le marché international.

Cette technologie influencera également l'environnement. Dans l'avenir, plus de gens deviendront concernés par l'environnement

147

parce que ce qui affecte l'environnement, affecte aussi la race humaine. En voyant cette nouvelle technologie de l'Ontario, la demande pour l'énergie solaire sera beaucoup plus élevée. Ainsi, les industries et les maisons utiliseront moins d'énergie pétrolière et plus d'énergie solaire. La couche d'ozone pourra se réparer plus vite et la planète regagnera sa santé perdue. Mais, ne vous inquiétez pas, les compagnies de pétrole ne seront pas éliminées. Elles produiront encore leur pétrole pour la construction des plastiques et des produits synthétiques. De cette manière, les gens qui travailleront dans cette industrie pourront conserver leurs emplois. En parlant des produits pétroliers et des plastiques, on peut se poser la question suivante: comment disposera-t-on des déchets sur la terre? Pour y répondre, il faut examiner certains phénomènes dans l'espace.

Ce à quoi je fais allusion sont les trous noirs. En théorie on croit que si un objet assez grand entrait dans un trou noir, l'objet serait tellement compressé par les forces de gravité qu'il rapetisserait pour n'être plus qu'une petite bille. En utilisant des fusées équipées par des voiles de vents solaires, on lancerait des déchets dans un trou noir où ils seraient compressés et, ainsi, nous pourrions vider la terre des déchets et des produits dangereux (déchets nucléaires, etc.).

Alors, les gens pourraient boire de l'eau fraîche, respirer facilement et vivre libres de tout déchet. Les recherches prouvent que quelques maladies, comme l'asthme et les problèmes de respiration, sont reliées à la pollution. Alors, si nous pouvions vider la terre des déchets et réparer la couche d'ozone, les maladies comme l'asthme seraient probablement moins communes parmi les citoyens canadiens.

C'est assez intéressant de prédire ce qui arrivera dans le futur. On peut s'attendre à presque n'importe quoi en Ontario en l'an 2020. Par exemple, en 1977, il y a presque 20 ans, Ken Olson, fondateur de Digital Equipment Corp., a dit, «Il n'y a aucune raison pour que quelqu'un veuille avoir un ordinateur à la maison.» Maintenant il y a plein de gens qui ont un ordinateur. Mes idées sont seulement des visions imaginatives et il n'est absolument pas sûr que ces événements arriveront. Elles ne sont que mes propres prédictions à propos du futur du Canada et de l'Ontario. Il y a des visions qui semblent presque impossibles à atteindre, mais on a vu au cours de l'histoire plusieurs occasions où la race humaine a vaincu ses dilemmes. N'est-ce pas vrai qu'on a mis un homme sur la lune? Alors, on ne sait pas vraiment à quoi s'attendre de l'Ontario de 2020. On peut quand même imaginer et espérer.

11e année / Grade 11
Lakehead District School Board

Matthew J. Peltoniemi

A Future Inventor

In the year 2020, I will be 27 years old. I want to be an Inventor. I will make life easier and it will cost less. My Invention will do jobs for people, especially people who are handicapped. I will make all sorts of things. Things that will help old and young.

Beeta Senedjani

Grade 2 / 2e année
Toronto District School Board

The Television of the Year 2020

Our group's invention of the year 2020 is a television. But don't get us wrong, this is no ordinary television. It is a four-screen TV that allows a minimum of four people to watch different channels all at once.

It is shaped as a cube and there is one screen on each side except for the top and bottom. The stand supporting the television is able to bend so it can fold down like an accordion to a preferable height for a table.

For our planning, we decided to do something that involved entertainment. We thought of pros and cons about our TV during the current year, 1999. A con was you can only watch one show on television. So we thought about adding three more screens. This led to a four-screen TV. For instance, say mom wanted to watch a soap opera, dad wanted to watch sports, older sister wanted to watch BET, and little brother wanted to watch The Learning Channel. Everyone could make the *Television of the Year 2020* convenient. Another thing we thought about during our planning was how will the future look in the year 2020. Our conclusion was the future would look funky. Therefore we decided to use funky colours. As you can see in our visual planning and model, we used four bright colours and black. We think we put a lot of thought into this television, which we think will be the *Television of the Year 2020*.

Our product can work by a few simple steps. Simply turn on the TV with the *Television of the Year 2020*'s remote control. The remote is not yet available but will be soon in stores everywhere. If you do not have a remote, the TV is voice activated but works with batteries ONLY. Voice activation includes buttons, channels, volume and power.

We feel that our television will change the lives of others. It will satisfy and end fights caused by television shows.

As you can see, we think that our invention will be a great success to the near future, the year 2020!!!

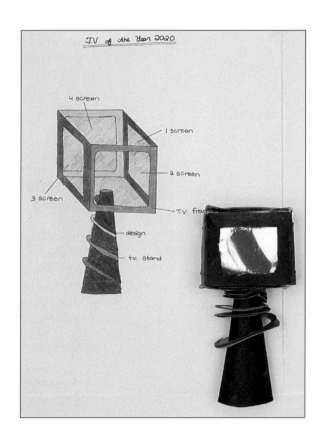

Mandy Bhamra
Divani Premraj
A.P.

Grade 8 / 8e année

Different Ways in 2020

One night on New Year's Eve of 1999 I started to wonder what kind of things would happen in the year 2020. I am nine right now, and I'll be thirty-one in the year 2020. Here are some of the ways that I think we are going to be different.

Travel

Walking Made Easy: The Conveyor Belt Sidewalk

A moving sidewalk did you ever hear?
It takes you places here and there!

It is a big conveyor belt which moves you along at a nice speed. Instead of walking, you would be riding along on a conveyor belt. When there is a road, you would just walk along to the next sidewalk and move along again. This is an electric powered machine and does not pollute the air. This would replace our ordinary grey sidewalk.

No More Traffic Jams: The Monorail

A monorail gliding way up high, way up, way up, way up in the sky,
Better than a train, and faster too, read about it, and you'll shout yahoo!

It's a car on a wire, not a car you drive. It's a train car and it takes you places faster than Via Rail. It is also electric, so it does not pollute the air. The wire does not move but the train car moves. Now people can get from home to work faster.

No More Smog: The Electric Car

No more engines screaming by, no more smog up in the sky,
Electric cars up on a track, back and forth, forth and back.

An electric car is one that you just have to pull onto a track and it drives on down the track. You don't need a steering wheel. All that you need to do is program the car to where you want to go and it takes you there. The track is exactly like a train track, only cars run on it. Now kids can sit in the driver's seat!

The Bicycle Times Two: The Quadcycle
Bicycles are in the past,
The quadcycle is the thing that will last.

The quadcycle is four wheeled, powered by pedals. It can reach speeds of up to 55 km/h. It is able to do this by using a five-speed transmission with overdrive. It is a pollution-free way of getting around in the year 2020!

The City

Climate Control: The Domed City

Some like it hot, some like it cold.
Whatever the pleasure, it's well known.
You'll find it all under the dome.

There are four kinds of cities under domes. Each has their own climate. Spring, winter, summer, or fall are all found under one of the domes. The most important job under the domes is working in the thermostat building, where the climate is controlled for the dome. In the building is the filtration system which keeps the air clean for the population under the dome. People live in one of the domes, but if they want to go to a different season, there are tunnels to one of the four domes. The houses look like a small tower. Inside, instead of stairs, there is an elevator to take you to the different levels. People will live comfortably under the domes.

Grade 3 / 3ᵉ année
Peterborough Victoria Northumberland
and Clarington Catholic District
School Board

James Dobos

152

La salle de classe en 2020

Léa Grond

2e année / Grade 2
Conseil scolaire du district
du Centre-Sud-Ouest

Life in the Year 2020

2020, 22 years from now, will be totally different! The moon won't be something we look at and dream what it's like up there, cancer will be just a memory, and the name Maxine McCurdy will be known throughout the world!

Commoners living on the moon! It won't be just astronauts going up there. Eventually, going to the moon for March Break will be like going to Florida! Some people will live on the moon, not that I want to. They will live in a giant dome (like on The Truman Show). Fake grass, fake sky, fake air! What would happen if Moon marines did live there? And started blasting the dome?

Cancer will be eliminated by me or someone else. Getting rid of it will be as easy as getting a flu shot or even easier. Medical technology will be greatly increased and for me (a future M.D.) to be famous all I have to do is cure the common cold! Even though I would rather cure cancer, but anything is good (one less reason to get sick).

Maxine J. McCurdy is a name that will go down in history (for what, I don't know). It will be known for wonderful things, maybe her medical discoveries as a doctor, maybe for one of her books, or maybe for her Academy Award for writing a wonderful movie. I don't know but somehow that name will be in a hall of fame.

I think that if all of these dreams of 2020 aren't made a reality by some Canadian somewhere, I don't know what will.

153

Grade 7 / 7ᵉ année
Limestone District School Board

Maxine McCurdy

Hearts

Taylor Goulet

Grade 3 / 3ᵉ année
Algoma District School Board

154

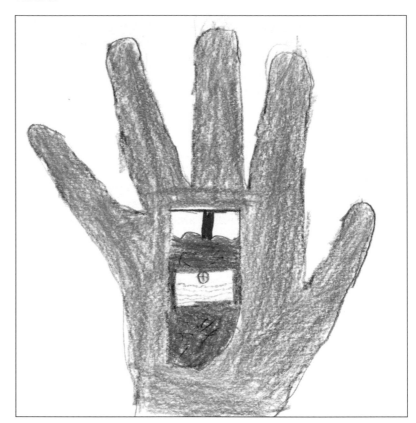

"Hearto", a special medicine that I will make, will help to make old hearts younger again.

My Ontario — Now and Then

In 2020 there will be flying cars.
Ontario will have big buildings.
We will know everything about space.
Maybe they will find an outer space planet that has people.
The computers will know everything.
There will be lots of people, that some people will have to
  live underground.
Some countries will break into pieces.
Then they will have to make new maps.
The police will be really cool.
There will be lots of taxi drivers.
The subways will be flying.
The trains will be flying too.
There will be suits that will make people fly.
I think these things will happen because day by day things get
  better and in twenty years they will be a lot better.

Grade 2 / 2ᵉ année
Peel District School Board

Rameez Imtiaz

In the Years to Come

Future. What is in store for all of humanity in the years to come? Will robots take over all of the industry? Will the world become a friendly and peaceful place? Will the Messiah return? This paper shows one way of looking at the earth in the year 2020.

It is Friday, April 16, 2020. I am a 34-year-old husband and father. My son, Josh, who is seven years old, has already left for school. My wife is working at her job in the Internet room in our house. I am just leaving to go to work in Toronto.

I get into a vehicle that I had designed. I started as an engineer of cars. It was my job to make cars safer and to be better for the environment. I, along with some other people, thought of some great ideas to make the cars safe. We decided that if we could keep the cars apart, the vehicles could not hit each other. This way there would be fewer accidents. In the side and rear of all of the cars we put opposite magnets. This is so that cars cannot get close to each other. The car manufacturers adapted this feature and it is now used in all new cars. Also to stop the heavy pollution from the car's exhaust, we redesigned the engine. We made it so that it was extremely fuel efficient. Cars can now travel 100 kilometres on only one litre of gas.

I have since been promoted to manager of the engineering section of the largest car company in the world. My job is to advance or terminate ideas that other people come up with. I have the last say in what goes in to production.

As I near my work in downtown Toronto, I pass mostly factories. There is big business in industry because after the robots are built to do their job there are very few costs. Only one-third of workers in factories are humans because of robots replacing jobs. I then pass a huge store that holds nearly everything that you would need. There is one large store every few blocks, but there are very few other stores because they cannot compete with the large stores.

I drive up to where I work, which is just one of the many factories. Even though there are so many robots there are many other jobs, too. The robots produce so much that there is a lot of work in packing and transporting the goods to the rest of the world. Also there is a space station just outside of Toronto that is independently owned which created jobs for thousands of people. The space station is currently working on a mission around Jupiter. With all of the factories, Ontario supplies many countries with different things.

The next day is Saturday so my wife and I decide to spend the day together as a family. We wanted to go to Wasaga Beach but the weather is not great and we do not want to drive. I go to the computer and type *Wasaga Beach* into the Internet. We enter the Internet room and my wife and I lie down on the beach. My son instantly runs down to play with the other kids in the water. The other kids are in their Internet rooms too and we are connected into the same place. I enjoy the safe heat and nap for a short time. This is the most popular way to relax now because it is safe, easy and comfortable. Also, you can go almost anywhere you choose.

On Sunday morning we wake up at 7 a.m. We get ready and go to eight o'clock mass. It was nearly the same as I had always remembered. My family received a great, uplifting mass from the woman priest. After we were given the host and the mass was finished, we went home.

Once we were home from church, I decided to make a turkey dinner with all of the fixings. I started to prepare 30 minutes before we were planning to eat. All of the vegetables were put into one appliance and were left to be peeled and sliced. I put the turkey in the ultra-heat oven and then got the vegetables and put them in too. About fifteen minutes later everything was cooked. We all sat and feasted; it was a great meal.

Monday morning I did not have to go to work until later so I drove my son into school. He is in his first year of school with the other kids who are seven. The starting age for school is older so that kids will already know the basics and will just have to learn the complicated things. He will learn very much in his first four years of junior school. After that he will go to high school for the next four years. When he is sixteen we plan to send him to university, so that he will have a better chance of getting a job. Now that companies had robots doing the manual jobs, there was mainly work in managing and other intellectual jobs. He will probably be done his schooling in ten to twelve years by the time he is eighteen. Then, hopefully, he will get a job.

This is just one way of looking to the future. Anything could happen, and in my opinion things will not drastically change in the next twenty years. Life will evolve as it always has. Humans will continue to thrive for a long time.

Grade 8 / 8ᵉ année
Simcoe Muskoka Catholic
District School Board

Stefan Andrushenko

2020 Poem

My prediction for the future
Has got to do with the past.
But what I say may not be right
Unless time passes fast.
Maybe they'll make flying cars
With less pollution for the world.
Or hovering vehicles with jet packs and rockets
But I hope they won't be covered in swirls.
This might be an over-populated country
All crowded and squished so tight.
So we'll build a city on the moon
I think that'll help, it just might.
If you're really lazy, and don't want to do much,
I think they'll construct homework machines.
But as you know, we all need jobs,
No jobless men or women, please!
Maybe there'll be disease control
When people get cured and don't die.
I wish there'd be no homeless people
So we can all live in peace and eat pie.
There might also be working robots
Like butlers and servants and maids.
But they'll probably be expensive
For the price might increase by days.
That's my 2020 poem
That's all I have to say.
It's done: The End — I quit!
I'd rather be eating hay.

Monica Chung

Grade 4 / 4e année
Peel District School Board

Mieux pour tous

le mardi, 13 avril 1999

En l'an 2020 tout va être changé. Il va y avoir des extra-terrestres différents sur Terre et pas juste des humains. On va utilise la technologie de ces créatures. À l'école on apprendra les langage de ses créatures. On ne pourrait peut être pas répéter ces langages mais on pourra les comprendre.

À l'école on va apprendre avec des lunettes 3 dimensions, ie=si on étudie la deuxième guerre mondiale, on mettra les lunettes et on sera dans le champ de bataille en train de regarder la bataille. À l'école les professeurs vont être des robots avec un "puce" électro'pour Enseigner et ça c'est tout.

Les aveugles vont aimer beaucoup leur vie en l'an 2020. Ils auront des lunettes qui les laissent voir comme tout le monde. Les personnes sourdes auront des petits pare-col électriques qui écriront ce qu'ils entendent. Les personnes muettes auront des machines qu'ils mettent dans ses dents comme des broche

Les machines permettront aux personnes muettes de parler.

En l'année 2020 le cancer va être comme la grippe d'aujourd'hui. Mais, il y aura d'autres maladies comme "le frérot" et "le cylone". les maladies seront contagieuses mais ne pourront pas te tuer. La médicine aura des pilules qui ont une "puce" électronique qui détruit les maladies. Les "puces" électroniques seront armés de zappeurs et de marteaux spéciaux pour éliminer les virus qui causent les maladies.

4e année / Grade 4
Ottawa-Carleton District School Board

Michael Scott

160

L'électricité

Je crois que dans l'ans 2020, l'énergie la plus importante sera l'éléctricité, ex-robot, auto. Il y aura des robots de toutes sortes des gros, des petits et des moyens. Ses robot vont être utiles pour les humains, il pourront aider à faire des opérations dans les hôpitaux. Pour faire les robots, il faudra au moins deux ans.

Bastien Ménard

5e année / Grade 5
Conseil scolaire du district catholique
de l'Est Ontarien

Samantha Choy

Grade 3 / 3e année
Peel District School Board

A Town under the Sea

I think in the year 2020, there will be a town underwater. People will have safety oxygen bins. Safety oxygen bins are in case they run out of air. You will be able to see the sea creatures. It will be fun under the sea with neighbours and friends. Also a food store will be there so you can buy food. There will be a school. The school is for learning. It is for ages 5 to 14.

There will be a hospital. The hospital is for hurt or sick people. To get to the surface or dry land, you would have to use a submarine. When you're on land, do what you want to, then take the submarine back underwater. If you move, then you put your stuff in the submarine and move to the land. If you just move to another home, just lift your furniture and take it through the tunnels to your new home. I will make it happen by studying it in school. If I don't, I will work with people to invent a town underwater.

Drawing of the "Rocket Pack"

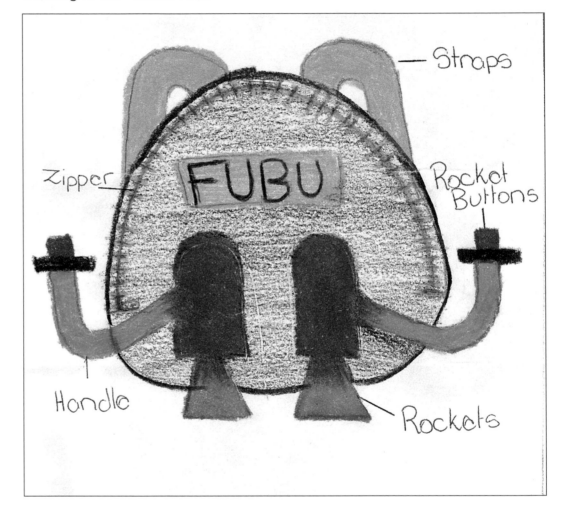

<u>The Rocket Pack</u>

This is a 21st century model of a "Rocket Pack." It is a new and improved way to get where you want to go in the matter of minutes. To use it, you simply: place the two straps on your shoulders, as you would do with a normal back-pack. The two handles with the buttons at the top are used to start the engines and direct you to where you would like to go. The Rocket Pack enables you to place all of your belongings in it, exactly like a normal back-pack would do. This picture would just be one of the hundreds of vibrant coloured Rocket Packs. They would especially be created for teens and young adults, but anyone would be able to use them. It is a fun and easy way to get anywhere you want to go. Have Fun!!

Grade 8 / 8e année
Peel District School Board

Melanie Padiachy

My Ontario in the Year 2020 Will Be Remarkable

What could My Ontario look and act like in the year 2020? I'm sure each and every one of these students that will be participating in My Ontario will have a different and intelligent idea on how this province will be in those 21 years from now. So I think that even I can't mess this one up. But seriously folks. What really could Ontario be like in the year 2020? Space ships that can fly through the galaxy? Skyscrapers that are taller than the Rocky Mountains? Or maybe robots that will do our daily chores for us? Of course no one really knows if any of this can happen, but as the late Gene Roddenbury said, "I do not believe that this beautiful world will go out in a big boom and a flash of light." And I for one think he was right.

But until we find out what my Ontario and the rest of the world will be like in 2020, here's my prediction.

- Transportation: A scientist from Canada will invent cars that will revolutionize the way we think about the environment. These cars will run on water. A renewable source of fuel that can drive an automobile for more than six miles with a single drop. These new engines will be coated with a special form of plastic that will reduce friction and almost eliminating the need for motor oil. Propeller airplanes will have no more use and are rarely used at all. While jets are still the main form of flight, the same scientist that invented the hydro-engine will be working with another team of scientists from all over the world to make a similar engine that can be used for airplanes. They will already have a prototype. However, all this amazing technology does not come without a price, there will be billions of dollars of the country's money that will have to be spent to replace and discard all these automobiles that need new engines.

- Environment: The environment will fortunately be slowly improving. The Ozone Layer was almost completely thinned out in some places around the year 2009. The governments of countries all over the world will have banned together to stop this problem. Unfortunately, all these countries could do nothing to control this environmental deterioration; the Polar Ice Caps begin to melt. A quarter of Greenland and several other arctic coasts will be engulfed in water around the year 2012. However this problem will start to repair itself, there will be a drastic change in 2014-2019. But the problem still remains, the Ozone is still dangerously thin and until we learn how to stop it, we'll just have to try and live with it.

165

- Technology: There will be amazing technological advances that will further the way we think, act, and work through our daily lifestyles. For educational purposes instead of using workbooks and pens, we will all use computers. These computers will have complete and total control of the school systems. Every student will have their own personal computers at their desk. For homework, students will take home specially fitted laptops that have tracking devices locked into them. These laptops can instantly download any file that is hooked up to it. And they will allow Internet access that can allow a student to look up any information that he or she needs. As far as weaponry goes, there are not a lot of weapons left because there is not a lot of need for them. Although there is still some violence left in the world, it has been made a law that any person found with a lethal weapon of any form will be charged with at the very least a few years in prison. But nucleonic weaponry is still a threat to many countries. In fact, it is no longer an uncommon thing for terrorists and especially governments to have nucleonic weaponry.

- Everyday Life: Humans still work, they still play, and they will still go to sleep every night and wake up every morning. But surprisingly in the year 2020, everyday life will be very different! Fortunately for moms, housework will be done by drones or "Robots." These drones will be programmed to work and act in a respectable manner. The drones will have many cleaning arms, an almost indestructible surface and a rechargeable power stand that will allow them to work on a fully powered stream. Women will be just as common as men in the workplace and will be rarely put down. School days will be only six hours long and recesses will be thirty minutes each. There will be two of them in a day and at least twenty minutes of free time each day. Money will still be the most important factor of keeping a household together. Both the father and the mother will contribute to keeping a household up and running. Families will be limited to having only five children maximum. There will be another international day added to the usual seven days we have at the present time. This day shall be called Funday and it allows every single person to get a day off. It is technically another day of the weekend.

My Ontario in the year 2020 will be a remarkable place, if any of my predictions some day turn to reality. Well I guess we will find out.

Grade 7 / 7e année
Hamilton-Wentworth District School
Board

Shawn McCarty

Progrès de la médecine

J'ai fait des nouvelles cures pour des maladies qui aujourd'hui en n'ont pas.

Spencer Allen Fauteux

3ᵉ année / Grade 3
Conseil scolaire du district des écoles
catholiques de Sud-Ouest de l'Ontario

Transportation
Le transport

167

168

Colourful Cars and Cool Styles

In 2020 I think there will be cars with five wheels and they will have different coloured stripes. In the middle of the tire it will be red. It will be the cool style. The door to the car will be blue. Some of the windows will be coloured. People will also change the way they write, because this is boring! The writing will look like this'

THIS

169

Grade 2 / 2ᵉ année
Peel District School Board

Caitlin Doyle

170

Bus Safety

In the year 2020 all school buses will have seatbelts for children's safety! They will also have springs under the seats for a comfortable ride, hooks to hang your jackets on, and TVs and stereos.

Danielle Nelson

Grade 4 / 4e année
Keewatin-Patricia District School Board

Flying Cars

What's our transportation in the year 2020?
I think that cars will probably fly.
I think that cars will fly really high.
You can see cars flying everywhere around
But you won't see cars driving on the ground.
When cars are flying, people will look down to see trains
If cars are flying very high they will even see planes.
If you listen you'll hear cars crashing somewhere
Then you'll know they were flying too fast in the air.
You'll see lots of different kinds of cars
Who knows, they might be flying to Mars!
When cars are flying, the birds must watch out
If birds are in your way, honk at them and shout.
If you run out of gas, your car will drop down
The people below will have a big frown.
You will hear flying car engines going *zeen, zeen*
If you want to drive you should be over nineteen.

171

Grade 4 / 4ᵉ année
Peel District School Board

Alex Timoon

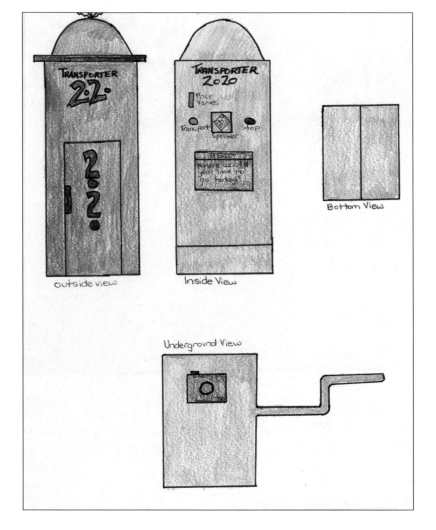

172

The Transporter of 2020

Directions:
1) Step into the transporter.
2) Insert price for travelling.
3) Tell the transporter where you would like to go by speaking into the speaker.
4) Press stop if you have made a mistake about something.
5) Once everything is correct, press transport, the bottom will open, and you will drop.
6) Once you drop, your picture will be taken and you will transport.

Narinder Mundi

Grade 8 / 8ᵉ année
Peel District School Board

Sky Transportation

Grade 6 / 6ᵉ année
Peel District School Board

Krista Peters
Amanda Rudnicki

Aquamobile

My artistic intentions include trying to illustrate what I think Ontario will look like in the year 2020, in a generally simple or abstracted image. My image looks at automotive alterations. Specifically, how cars are fueled. My artwork portrays my theory that in the year 2020, cars running on water will be the status quo/ordinary. It has already been proven possible and I feel by the year 2020, a method of manufacturing this type of vehicle will have been discovered that is easier, less expensive, and less time-consuming.

To reach the completion of this piece, I was required to make many artistic choices. For instance, what would be the area of emphasis/focal point, and how would I show it? Well, to show the point of emphasis, I painted the car with a metallic silver and made it distinctly large. I also put detail into the futuristic design of a car. The station is also part of the focal point. It is painted with a dark colour, and is fairly detailed. I wanted the rest of the piece to be fairly simple and light so that the area of dominance would really *shine* through. If someone were to look at the painting, their eyes would circle around the page, and rest on the car and station. I thought silver would be the ideal colour for the car since silver is a new colour for a car. I thought red would be the perfect colour for use on the station. I liked the angle at which the car (and the station) are placed. It adds a 3-Dimensional ambience to the piece. The elements I thought to include in this piece were:
- texture/pattern
- shape/form
- value
- movement
- space
- line

The principles included:
- balance (symmetrical)
- contrast
- emphasis

In the year 2020, I envision myself as the driver of an "Aquamobile." Not only is this vehicle environmentally friendly, but it's consumer friendly. To buy water would be much cheaper than to buy gas. There would also be different types of fuel water to choose from. There could be tap water, spring water, and/or filtered water. They would have different costs, but they would all be relatively cheap.

There is one problem I see with this idea. Gas stations will most likely make less money for a few reasons:

1. The water would cost less.

2. Most people would have their own bottles of water to refill their tank. However, there is a positive reaction. Water companies would all profit. The demand for water would increase.

The main issue would be reducing pollution (in the air) and this would reduce the level of air pollution dramatically.

Grade 7 / 7ᵉ année
Peel District School Board

Danielle Sandhu

176

A. We think that cars will be faster in the year 2020 then the standerd modern day car. We think that the standerd modern day car, like a Honda Civic, It will be just as fast as a Dodge vijen, or a car that has two jet engines.

B. We usd hot colours to show speed. And we over lapped the car, so it looks like it is going fast. And we made the shape of the car different so it looks like it is more futuristic.

C. I envision My Self as a sports thrapist, or if I get lucky, a baseball player. But living in Canada, I don't really have a chance Shaun envisions him self as a basketball player.

Racing into Technology

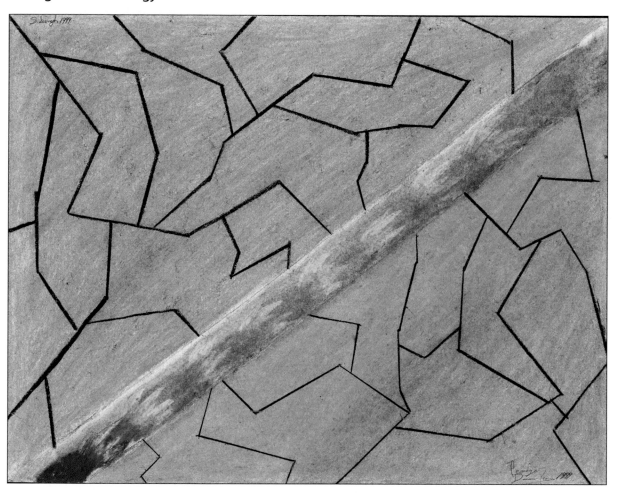

177

Grade 7 / 7e année
Peel District School Board

Shaun Singh
George Dimacakos

Car of the Future

Our car, the TH Super 2020 deluxe model, is above all the standards of even the best cars built to date. First let's take a look at how the car runs. Instead of an engine, the car has hover pads located along the bottom of the car. These allow the car to hover above the ground at two feet while in motion. Another amazing feature about our car is that it is controlled by magnets, both positive and negative charges, evenly located on the bottom of the car. These attract and distract from all negative charge magnets on the road. A pedal inside the car increases the charge of the magnets on the car, hence increasing or decreasing the speed at which you travel. The car also has special non-glare lights on the front and back of the car. These prevent oncoming cars from being momentarily blinded from your bright lights. Also with the use of magnets, the door/windshield/roof of the car is opened, closed, and locked. Installed on the bottom of the door is a positive charged magnet and installed in the car is a half positive, half negative charged magnet which can rotate around with the push of a button. When the car magnet is switched to negative the door locks to the car. When it is switched to a positive charge the door unlocks and opens slowly to prevent damage. When the door is open and the magnet is switched to a negative charge, the magnet on the door is pulled to the car, closing firmly.

Exterior View
Front of Car

1) High power lights installed on the outside of each dual-lamp projection device are the highest in quality, and brightest lamps on the market.
2) Lower positioned Trio-lamps give the driver and passenger(s) optimum safety.
3) This is the revolutionary microchip identity plate. The driver's license, name and any necessary ID is under this device. If this information is needed, the authority simply scans the plate with a micro-scanner, and everything is done quickly and easily.
4) These blinker systems are also very high in quality. They give off enough light to see them two kilometres down the road.
5) These storage compartments can hold enough weight to carry a large cow to the chosen destination. They are unique in many ways.

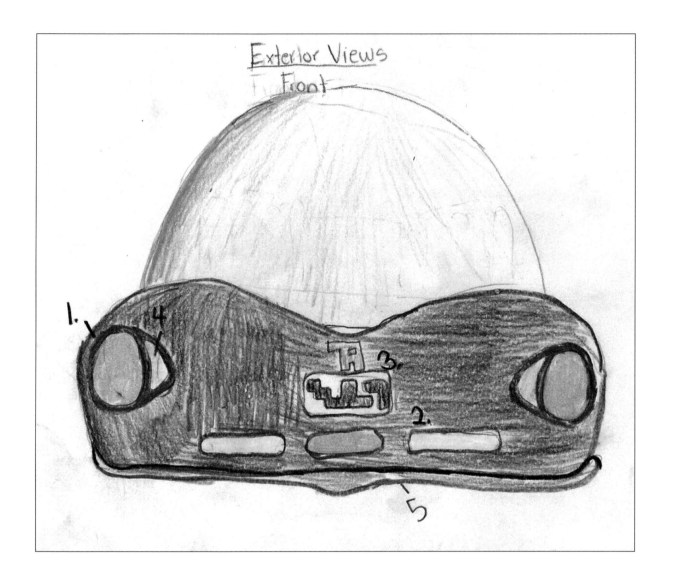

Grade 8 / 8ᵉ année
York Region District School Board

Kevin Hudson
Trevor Fahlgren

The Millennium Highway

Daniel Huber

Grade 6 / 6ᵉ année
Dufferin-Peel Catholic District School
Board

Revolutionary Rapid Transit

Grade 7 / 7ᵉ année
Niagara Catholic District School Board

Mackenzie Kish

182

We live in Northwestern Ontario. Our Parents drive us all over the place on small roads. Sometimes there are snowstorms that make it hard to drive. Sometimes there are flash floods that ruin the roads. As we get older and smarter we will have the chance to make better cars and roads. When we are older and driving, the sensors in the roads will make traveling in Northwestern Ontario safer for us and our children. The sensors will prevent accidents because the cars will not hit each other.

Danielle's 2020 Car

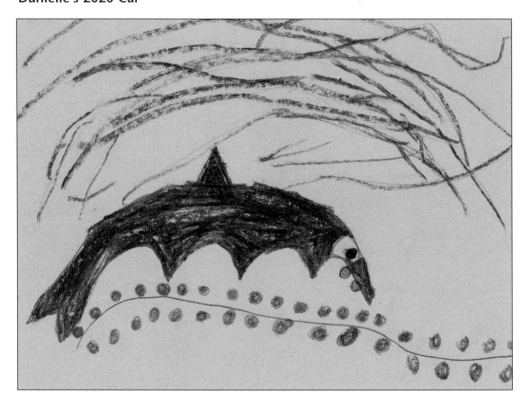

My car is like a dolphin and it can go very fast. And it can go 1001. You don't have to drive. You are probably thinking why I don't have to drive. It is because there are little sensors and it has a computer. We have to type where we are going and it would go where we want it to go. If you don't type where you want to go, it won't go. What makes it go is a little computer.

Danielle Zborowski
Grade 1 / 1ʳᵉ année
Superior North Catholic
District School Board

183

Micaela's 2020 Car

My Banana Lunch Car has a computer that can make me go from place to place and I don't even have to drive there. I have an antenna on the top of my Banana Lunch Car. That's why my car is called the Banana Lunch Car. My car has a red sensor and a green sensor. When I program my computer I put Schreiber to Thunder Bay and my car will go there. It will follow the red sensors on the road to go anywhere. To return home my vehicle will follow the green sensors. This is all done by a special computer. My Banana Lunch Car has five tires to run on and you have to keep them balanced.

Grade 2 / 2ᵉ année
Superior North Catholic
District School Board

Micaela Commisso

Jorie's 2020 Car

In the year 2020 I think this is what a car is going to look like. In this car you can go to sleep when the car is moving. You can watch TV. When you want to go somewhere, type where you want to go into the computer. As you see there are two compartments on my car. You can sit on the roof. The car moves with sensors. On the bottom of the car there are two sensors.

184

Jorie Gionet
Grade 1 / 1re année
Superior North Catholic
District School Board

Doriana's 2020 Car

In the year 2020 my truck is going to have sensors and it will have a computer. It is called the Rainbow Truck. The computer controls the truck. The sensors follow the road. It has a refrigerator so the passengers can relax and eat while my truck is following the sensors down the road. You do not have to drive the truck. It also has wings so it can fly over traffic jams.

Grade 1 / 1ʳᵉ année
Superior North Catholic
District School Board

Doriana Veneziano

La voiture de policier en l'an 2000

Le bus pompier 2000 pour éteindre les feux.

Alain Collin

L'ambulance 2000 pour transporter les malades.

Julie Veronneau

186

La voiture 2000 pour les policiers.

JEFFREY Poulin

Alain Collin
Julie Veronneau
Jeffrey Poulin

2e année / Grade 2
Conseil scolaire de Gogama

Environment
L'environnement

187

Metropolismillennium

Colin Saunders   Grade 4 / 4ᵉ année

Environment Day

In 2020 none of our people will smoke, pollute or kill our animals for sport or fun. They will share the streets, help the poor and always obey the rules. To get it this way, I will ask the provincial government to let all our people out of work or school for one day. We will put up lots of signs and clean up our environment. I hope it works because I want every person to have a clean Ontario to live in.

189

Grade 3 / 3ᵉ année
Durham Catholic District School Board

Michael D. Davies

No Littering

MY ONTARIO

In the year 2020, the air will be clean and there will be no Pollution. I plan to help by not littering on the ground.

Alyssa Young

Grade 5 / 5ᵉ année
York Region District School Board

Feu de forêt

Le réchauffement de la planète occasionnera des feux de forêt.

191

Red Lake Area Combined
Roman Catholic Separate School Board

Harmony Hood

192

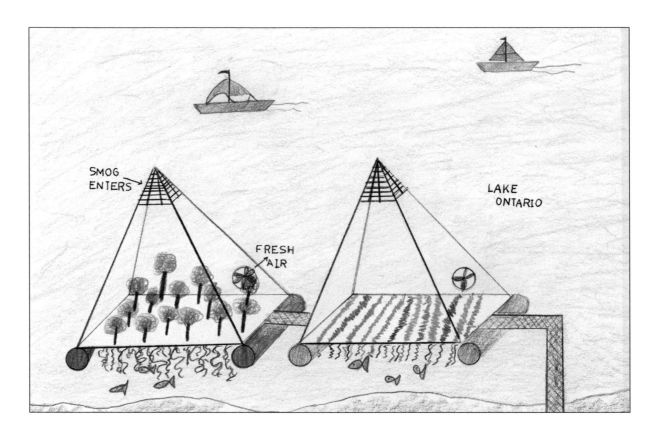

My Ontario Hydroponics Centre for 2020

In the year 2020 I would like to be an architect and design a Hydroponics Centre to grow plants in. I really like to build and design structures and think that a place to help the environment would be very useful in Ontario's future. The Centre would be a glass pyramid that grows plants. It would float on top of Lake Ontario with the plant roots dangling into the water. There would be no soil needed for the plants. The plants would use the water and sunlight to grow. I would grow vegetables and fruits and trees. The plants could grow faster and produce more. I wouldn't need expensive machinery to farm them, like tractors. The plants would help clean the air in the dome and filter polluted lake water and make the water clean. No bugs could come inside on the plants so I don't need to use harmful sprays or pesticides on the plants. This could also help make more jobs for farmers and people who could help me take care of the plants and sell products from them.

Brian Liska

Grade 5 / 5e année
Dufferin-Peel Catholic
District School Board

Natural Attraction

In Ontario where the winds blow
And the flowers grow
The trees are many
And the lakes are plenty
Where the summers are hot
And the winters are cold
Ontario is the place
I'll be when I'm old.

Grade 5 / 5ᵉ année
Lakehead District School Board

Landon W. Rees

193

Everything Will Be Plastic

I believe that by the year 2020 everything will be made from
plastic. I mean everything: cars, trucks, fridges, stoves, pots
and pans. I mean everything.

  Plastics will be everywhere: even houses and buildings will be
made from plastic. The best part will be that everything will be
recycled into something else for us to use. Because of all the plastic
there will be less metals. Less metal will mean less pollution in the
air and water. This will make the fish happier. The air we breathe
will be cleaner and everyone will be happy. There will be more
flowers to smell and bigger trees to climb.

  This is what I think it will be like in Ontario in the year 2020.
A happier and better place to live.

Grade 2 / 2ᵉ année
Dufferin-Peel Catholic
District School Board

Ben Syme

194

My Ontario

In the year 2020 I will be 28. I will help Ontario get rid of all the pollution. I think to make Ontario a better place for everyone, young and old, should appreciate their surroundings. Ontario is a beautiful province, and every citizen and all big companies must work hard to keep our waters, land, and air clean for our future generations.

by: Nikki Feige

Keep Ontario Clean

Grade 2 / 2ᵉ année
Toronto District School Board

Nikki Feige

The Great Ontario

The Great Ontario

On riverbanks, in lakes and forests green,
Nature grows protected.
Today the air is sparkling clean,
All the loons cry happily.
Right and justice means: no homeless-food for everyone.
Imagine a province without garbage and crime—
Ontario!

Matthew Kalant-Kelling
Grade 3 / 3ᵉ année
Toronto District School Board

196

As the Century Turns. . .

I think that in the year 2020 everyone in school will have a laptop computer instead of notebooks. Then, kids will only have to carry the computer, disks, one for each subject, a book, and sometimes gym clothes. There won't be any lockers either, just hooks to hang up coats. There will be the same subjects at school, but everyone will have to learn to type and use computers when they are little. They could probably teach with computers from grade one all the way through high school.

Transportation in 2020 will be the same as now, but it will not pollute the air. People will find a way to make either solar or water-powered cars, buses, planes, and everything else that makes pollution. Anybody who drives a vehicle that pollutes will be fined a lot of money. Companies that still make those vehicles will also be fined.

Also, people will find a way to get rid of all the pollution in Ontario. They will use a huge vacuum that sucks up everything that pollutes. After they use it once, they will make a *very* strict law that no one can pollute in any way. If people pollute, they will get fined for lots and lots of money, even just for dropping garbage. The vacuum will just be saved for emergencies, which will never happen.

Most companies won't make garbage any more in 2020. Only about one percent of the garbage produced now will still be produced then. Everything else will either be eliminated, or will be able to be recycled.

All mail going out of Ontario, or coming into Ontario, will be carried on very fast planes that don't pollute. It will never take more than a day to deliver any letter or package.

I will help Ontario in 2020 by being a pilot. I will fly a plane that doesn't pollute. When all the people in the places I fly to see my plane, they will also want a plane like mine. That way, other places will not make as much pollution as they do now.

I hope that we can make all these things come true, maybe even before 2020.

197

Grade 6 / 6ᵉ année
Halton District School Board

Sam Hobbes

198

Conservation

The reason I painted a wilderness scene was because in 2020 we will still need the forests, and more and more of our forests are disappearing every day and we need to save our world.

Julie Adam

Grade 5 / 5ᵉ année
Catholic District School Board
of Eastern Ontario

Pollution Ontario

I would like to see Ontario be pollution free in the year 2020. We can all make it happen if we all don't litter, smoke, riding your bike whenever possible and car pooling. I will help by picking up litter, by riding my bike, by not smoking, and let people know we have to take care of our province.

Grade 3 / 3ᵉ année
Trillium Montessori School, Orangeville

Marcus El-Sarraf

199

Shaping Our Future Together

In the year 2020 I will be 30 years old.

I hope that there will still be dark green grass, beautiful flowers, healthy trees and a lot less pollution. I think that maybe we should bike-ride more often and use cars that run on cleaner fuels. We should stop dumping waste in our waters and contaminating our planet. We need to find better ways of cleaning it.

I will help make my wishes come true by staying in school and becoming a scientist. That way I can invent new ways to keep our environment clean.

In order to shape our future together as a planet we need to learn how to keep our environment clean.

Grade 5 / 5ᵉ année
Simcoe County District School Board

Eryn Whitter

Un parc

Les parcs ressembleront sensiblement à ceux que l'on connaît de nos jours.

S. Budweg

8e année / Grade 8
Red Lake Area Combined
Roman Catholic Separate School Board

Making My Reality

As the monorail slides across the slick oily track, the children play and look down, seeing people in their cars trying to keep up to the fast speed of the monorail.

I sit on the monorail and look into the distance and see green trees against the sky while the sun sets. The trees make a beautiful mix with yellow and orange. "Those three colours look beautiful together," I say to myself as the sun gets replaced by the moon. It will be a matter of time before I make it to the crystal clear Lake Ontario while the sun falls into the Great Lake. Soon I will be able to scuba dive with no fears of pollution in Lake Ontario.

In 2020 I will be 29. I hope to have an effect on Ontario. This way I will make these three points become reality. More trees, less pollution, and an all-Ontario monorail system. I will make more trees a reality by starting a club about getting more trees. That will make most of Ontario believe that it would be better if we had more trees. So every time we cut down a tree, we would have to plant more than one. For less pollution I would ask factories to use solar and wind power and the same thing for every other thing that requires power. This will help the water and the sky to get cleaner. I will make an all-around-Ontario monorail because there will probably be more people in Ontario. That would make them want a monorail.

I will be an engineer. That will help me know how to do all these things.

Grade 3 / 3ᵉ année   **Michael Vannelli**

202

No Pollution

In the year 2020 I want there to be no pollution so we can breathe clean air.

Jessica Emily Taylor

Grade 3 / 3e année
Peel District School Board

Don't Be a Litterbug

This ladybug and her friend are picking up trash on The ground. Ontario will be cleaner for bugs and people. Jennifer grade 3

203

204

Ontario's Dream by Ryan

Good morning Ontario, nice and clean,
That's what I want for our future dream,
To have more natural and original plains,
To have electric cars and unpolluted air,
That's what I want for Ontario's Dream!

Ryan Low   Grade 5 / 5ᵉ année

You'll Like What You See

In The Year 2020

In the year 2020 there are many things I want,

Bikes, car pools and buses and littering to stop!

When it rains there will be no acids in the air,

The plants will mop it up and bloom

In answer to our prayer.

We must remember to recycle

And that must always be.

And in the year 2020 you will like what you see.

Grade 2 / 2ᵉ année
Catholic District School Board
of Eastern Ontario

Alana Sargeant

205

How to Make Wishes Come True

We are the children of the new millennium. We should cherish it now, because it only comes around every thousand years. In the year 2020, or in about twenty years, I believe the new millennium will be overdone and forgotten. Time can do so many good *and* bad things. In the time of twenty-one years, this is what I think will happen.

I believe people will be much more stressful and busy. Why? Well, because so many things have built up, and all of it is finally blowing up in everyone's faces. For example, there will be so many endangered species, people will be on their toes to name the next dying-out animal. People then will start campaigns to save that particular animal, and others will do things to make sure that everything in their schedule isn't hurting any of them. Another example is our air pollution. As a result of the pollution, global warming will take action. In the last 1,600 years, our worldwide average temperature has risen only five degrees Celsius. It is now predicted that in about fifty years, the temperature will rise another five degrees. Then people will try to do their jobs, and make sure everything they buy and do is O.K for the environment. It will also look much busier because our population is rising very quickly, and it won't be long until Ontario will look like a mall on Saturday night.

Ontario, along with the rest of the world, will be much more electronic. Right now, almost everybody in my class has a computer. Soon high technological electric cars will revolutionize cars forever and save the environment, unless it's too late. With new toasters, bread will take 30 seconds to toast, and because of the busy people in two decades, and all the technology, more breakfast bars will be created. The newest computers will not have keyboards, but a microphone that writes whatever you say.

In twenty-one years, I wish time did only good things. I wish pollution could be absolutely exterminated in twenty-one years. I wish there could be world peace (or at least province peace)

206

with humans and animals in 21 years. I wish that although we will be heavily populated, everything and everyone would be organized and running smoothly. I wish that no one would ever be stressful because everyone would enjoy work, and never go to their jobs because they had to, but because they wanted to. I also wish, to conclude my dream, that I would be Ontario's premier, making sure all my standards are reached.

That is but a vision. A wild fantasy in someone's mind, and in my case, it has no chance of actually happening. To help this dream become close to my day-to-day life, I will encourage all to work hard but when they have worked hard enough I will give vacations. That way, people will hopefully enjoy working at my law firm because they will want a well-earned vacation. I will donate constantly to charities and Save the Animals places. I will recycle, buy Styrofoam or plastic things that say somewhere on the purchased item "No CFCs" and encourage everyone to do the same.

This project was assigned to students so they could "personally commemorate the dawn of the new millennium by sharing their vision." "To get involved in this once-in-a-lifetime event." To basically give students the chance to express their opinions on what will happen, and what they hope to have happen, in the year 2020. This English project was to give students a voice loud enough to reach the Government of Ontario. My voice probably won't go that far, but I'd like to say, for the twelve years I've had a brain, nothing has pleased me more than getting what I wanted. My vision, crazy as it may be, is what I want and I'm sure that most of Ontario wants it too. For wishes to come true, you have to do something about it, and in order to get somewhere, you have to work together. So, if everybody works together, and if everybody does a good job, and if everybody knows and enjoys what he or she are doing, then Ontario will succeed.

207

Grade 7 / 7ᵉ année
Hamilton-Wentworth
District School Board

Gloria Huh

208

Pollution in the Year 2020

Hi, my name is Stephanie Grace Battieste from Robert J. Lee P.S. in Brampton, Ontario. In my picture it is showing that in 1999 it is not as polluted as I think it will be in the year 2020. All of the beautiful flowers, plants, and grass will die because of the air and water pollution. If we all do our part and work together, hopefully by the year 2020 it won't be as bad as I think it might be.

Thank you.

Stephanie Battieste

Grade 7 / 7e année
Peel District School Board

Mon Ontario

Avec les chutes Niagara,
On est au centre du Canada.
Grâce aux belles grandes forêts,
On visera tous pour le succès.

Refrain :

La capitale est Toronto,
Et, on est riche en minéraux.
En 2020, les Ontariens,
Pourront aller loin et seront biens.

Refrain

Si on désire un beau futur,
Sauvegardons notre nature,
Surtout l'érable honorable,
Avec son bon sirop d'érable.

Refrain

Quand ce sera la nuit sur l'étang,
Les gens vivront de très beaux moments.
Les grands lacs et notre nature,
Aideront les gens dans le futur.

Refrain

À tous les endroits touristiques,
Les centres seront fantastiques.
Science-Nord et le grand Cinq Cent,
Les grandes villes, la Tour CN.

Refrain

Le bilinguisme est très génial.
C'est une province spéciale.
Notre beau drapeau est un honneur.
Il nous assure un bon bonheur.

Amanda Desaulnier
Amanda Ashley Martin
André Beaudette
Angèle Lafontaine
Chad Boucher
Chantal Brunet
Crystal McGee
Corey Gosselin
Eric Zachary
    Poulin Robinson
France Poulin
Janick Landry
Jesse Lee Lauzon
Joël Marc Perreault
Kerry Lynne Rhéaume
Kevin Dutrisac
Kevin Montpellier
Kyle M.
Lisa Michelle
    Castonguay
Luc Lagacé
Manon Lavoie
Marc Duchesne
Marie-France Grenier
Mélissa Bishop
Monik Anne Chénier
P. Albert
Pierre
Rémi Marcel Boucher
Sophie-Ann

5e année / Grade 5

Recipe for Year 2020

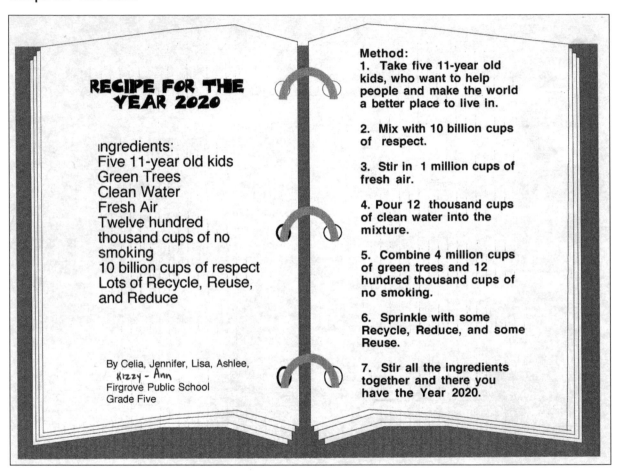

RECIPE FOR THE YEAR 2020

Ingredients:
Five 11-year old kids
Green Trees
Clean Water
Fresh Air
Twelve hundred thousand cups of no smoking
10 billion cups of respect
Lots of Recycle, Reuse, and Reduce

By Celia, Jennifer, Lisa, Ashlee, Kizzy-Ann
Firgrove Public School
Grade Five

Method:
1. Take five 11-year old kids, who want to help people and make the world a better place to live in.

2. Mix with 10 billion cups of respect.

3. Stir in 1 million cups of fresh air.

4. Pour 12 thousand cups of clean water into the mixture.

5. Combine 4 million cups of green trees and 12 hundred thousand cups of no smoking.

6. Sprinkle with some Recycle, Reduce, and some Reuse.

7. Stir all the ingredients together and there you have the Year 2020.

Jennifer Drepaul
Celia Lopez
Ashlee Ramsumeer
Kizzy-Ann Taylor
Lisa Truong

Grade 5 / 5e année
Toronto District School Board

If I Were Boss

If I were the boss of Ontario it would be clean....

There would be cars that took water not gas.

Every Friday, schools will clean up their yard.

For everybody who cuts down a tree, they would plant two more
and if they cut down two, they would plant four more.

Grade 5 / 5ᵉ année
York Region District School Board

Emily

212

Planting Trees

By the year 2020, in Ontario there will be a lot
more trees. I will help this happen by planting
a tree each year in honour of my birthday.

Nicholas Botticella

Grade 1 / 1ʳᵉ année
Trillium Lakelands District School Board

A Clean Earth

Grade 3 / 3e année
District School Board of Niagara

Jessica

214

Out My Window

This is what I want my Ontario to look like in 2020. I just want to look out my window and see trees and wildlife. I am going to try to have this happen by making wildlife reserves and planting a lot of trees.

Frank Callaghan

Grade 5 / 5ᵉ année
Wayside Academy
Peterborough

En l'an 2020 en Ontario

Refrain 1

En l'an 2020, ce sera beau
Parce que finalement propre
Sera l'eau.

Couplet 1

En l'an deux mille vingt.
Tout le monde aimera prendre des bains.
Parce que l'eau aura été filtrée.
Parce que ce sera de l'eau propre.
La, la, la, la, la
De l'eau propre
La, la, la, la, la.

Refrain

Couplet 2

Faudra vraiment faire attention.
Moi je ramasserais la pollution.
Ce sera comme si les fusils n'ont jamais existé.
Ils seront tous confisqués.

Refrain

Couplet 3

Il fera plus chaud qu'avant en Ontario.
Les pins ressembleront beaucoup au sapin.
«La taïga» sera nommée «La forêt boréale.»
«La forêt boréale» sera nommée «La Taïga.»

Refrain 2

J'aurai 31 ans mais ce ne sera vraiment pas
étonnant.
Parce que partout dans la ville.
Tout sera complètement débile.
Dé, dé, dé, débile
Débile, débile, débile.
Ohoait!!!
Sauf Moi.

Geneviève

5ᵉ année / Grade 5

215

Amey's Story

ONTARIO 2020
Nature

In 20 years from now the trees will be twice as strong and 3 times the size. The animals will be running all over the place. There will be a law against killing rabbits and such. The hunters will only be able to shoot 1 animal per year until there is too many and enough for everyone. The forest will be thicker than fat on a bear. The lakes will be as clear as glass. There will be fish as big as a Great Danes and the little fish will be healthy and strong. There won't be any garbage laying around. It will all be recycled or reused. I hope that this story of mine will come true and I hope you wish this too.

By Amey

216

Amey Belanger

Grade 5 / 5e année

Our Ontario – Pointing to the Future

The future of 2020
Is what we see here.
The future of 2020
Is very near.
At the top we have forgotten
At the bottom we have a dream
A dream we have made.
The new is in, the old is a fade.
To show the old, this is our way
Because we don't want it like today.
Nature is a part of it, not just us.
The animals don't whine or make a big fuss.
We whine about pollution and trash
But almost everyone cares about cash.
Ontario is the place to be.
It's a home for you and me.
This is how we think it might be.

217

Meagan Miseresky
Katie Bugden

Grade 5 / 5e année
Toronto Catholic District School Board

Motorway

A) Our Artistic Intention is showing that there
will still be farmland in the year 2020. It is
also showing a clean and healthy lifestyle to
live in. We have green grass, clear air, healthy
animals, and blue lakes and rivers.

B) We chose to use clean colour for the grass,
trees, sky, and sun. Also more dull or dirty
colours for the dirt and crop area. We chose
these shapes, colours, and layout because it
shows a very old and rustic scene.

C) We see ourselves as being a Computer
Animationist (Kevin) and a pilot (M.Robinson)
because those are the jobs we are interested in.

219

Grade 7 / 7ᵉ année   **Kevin Hutchinson**
Peel Distirct School Board   **M. Robinson**

Une chanson pour l'Ontario en 2020

Véronique Millaire

5e année / Grade 5
Conseil scolaire du district catholique
de l'Est Ontarien

Notre nature c'est l'Ontario

NOM: SAMANTHA CALLAGHAN
NIVEAU: 1re Année

École Frère-André
400, rue Base Line Ouest
London (ON)
N6J 1W1

221

1re année / Grade 1
Conseil scolaire du district des écoles
catholiques de Sud-Ouest de l'Ontario

Samantha Callaghan

A Safe and Peaceful World

I have a few things I wish would happen in the future:
I wish we would recycle, then throw things in the garbage.
I wish we threw garbage in garbage cans.
I want us to clean up parks when they are dirty.
There should be less factories.
There should be no pollution in the air.
There should be less smokers.
Everybody should care for mother earth.
People should make more recycled paper.
We shouldn't cut down as much trees as we do now.
We should use up both sides on a piece of paper.
We should help clean water when oil is in it.
More people should care for sick animals.
We should not bomb each other's countries.
Don't dirty the water, keep it clean.
Don't waste pencils because you waste trees.
We should help the poor and the elderly.
Don't rape or rob people.
Constructors should make better homes.
Other languages should be on TV.
Keep the air clean because now we have a hole in the ozone layer.
If we can do all this, we will have a safe and peaceful world.

222

223

Grade 5 / 5ᵉ année
Toronto Catholic District School Board

Dragana Glavas

Embellissement de la forêt

Les forêts seront plus belles à cause des plantations et du soin qu'on y apportera.

224

Hillary Hood

7e année / Grade 7
Red Lake Area Combined
Roman Catholic Separate School Board

Where We Live
Notre milieu de vie

Welcome to Ontario – We'll Make You Feel Incredible!

When I think ahead to what my province will be like in the year 2020, many possibilities come to mind. I think not so much of what Ontario will be like, but of what it could be like. Today I see Ontario as the economic, educational, industrial, technical and cultural capital of Canada. In the year 2020, I see an Ontario that has continued as the national leader in all these areas, and then some. I believe that it is within the power of every Ontarian to work toward a province where tourism is booming, industry is at an all time high and unemployment at an all time low, and where the "Canadian culture" is flourishing.

I predict that in the year 2020, Ontario will be attracting more tourists than ever before. This province possesses a kaleidoscope of rich, natural beauty. To paraphrase the words of my mother, "There is no place in the world as beautiful as Ontario in September." Every season ushers in a new diversity of landscape, from the sweeping crimsons of autumn to the sparkling lakes in summer. When I reflect on this beauty, I am surprised that more tourists do not come to Ontario. I believe it is only a matter of time before this changes. With every year that passes, technology becomes a greater part of our everyday lives. By the year 2020, I believe more people will be searching for place of escape.

Where better to go than one of Ontario's many provincial parks? I believe that our parks will become a haven for thousands of technology-weary tourists. There are also the promising possibilities of winter tourism. Although many Ontarians groan and complain abut the long winters, this season provides many tourist opportunities. It is exhilarating to spend a January (or December, or February, or March) afternoon gliding through virgin powder, admiring the sharp beauty of white snow against blue sky. Although many tourists already enjoy the winter activities Ontario offers, there are thousands of others who do not yet realize how much they would relish a winter vacation in Ontario. It is up to all Ontarians to work together in raising awareness of the vast variety of vacation possibilities which our province offers. I believe we can accomplish this. In doing so we will ensure that, by the year 2020, Ontario tourism will be flourishing.

Ontario already has a booming industry. By the year 2020, Ontario could have an industry that makes what we have now look like a few lemonade stands. With the economy steadily improving, the future looks bright for industrial Ontario. The presence of many internationally renowned universities will continue to attract intelligent and talented youth from all over the world. The resources of the national and provincial capitals will only increase Ontario's appeal to young students. When these students graduate from university or college, whatever their field, Ontario's corporations will be responsible for snatching them up before they have the chance to look elsewhere. With these educated young people driving the future of Ontario's industry, there will be a consistent decrease in unemployment. I believe the key to a booming industry in 2020 lies with the current industries working to ensure that all secondary school graduates are immediately provided with jobs.

With the dawn of the twenty-first century, I believe Ontario will take a leading role in the ongoing definition of the elusive Canadian culture. Canada has a multi-ethnic culture, which is most easily defined as a harmonious blending of many different races and cultures. Given Ontario's central position within the country, as well as the presence of the nation's capital, Ontario will be responsible for encouraging the expression of the Canadian identity. There are several ways in which our province could do so. The construction of museums which deal exclusively with the issue of Canadian culture and identity could serve to increase national awareness. Also, the

introduction of Canadian culture courses into the education system would set an example for the rest of the country. Of course, the preservation and teaching of national history will be an essential component of raising cultural awareness. Ontario must continue to ensure that national and provincial heritage sights are give top priority. Most importantly, the provincial government must see that Canadian history courses are mandatory throughout public school, for it is only through understanding our past that we may comprehend the events of the present.

Whenever I return from visiting my relatives in the U.S.A., I am greeted by a large sign at the base of the Gananoque bridge which reads, "Welcome to Ontario — We'll make you feel incredible!" It is when I see this sign that I know I am truly home. I am proud to be a resident of this beautiful province, which has so much to offer Canada and the world. It is my sincere hope that all Ontarians will work together to make the Ontario of 2020 one where tourism is booming, industry is high and unemployment low, and the Canadian culture is thriving. It is within our abilities to accomplish these goals. We need only to join forces with the interests of our province at heart. It is my belief that Ontario will continue to make people feel incredible for years to come.

227

OAC
Upper Canada District School Board

Broze Steggles

Joy and Peace

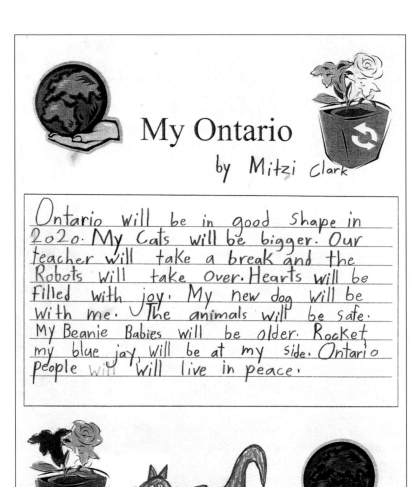

My Ontario

by Mitzi Clark

Ontario will be in good Shape in 2020. My Cats will be bigger. Our teacher will take a break and the Robots will take over. Hearts will be filled with joy. My new dog will be with me. The animals will be safe. My Beanie Babies will be older. Rocket, my blue jay, will be at my side. Ontario people will will live in peace.

228

Mitzi Clark

Grade 2 / 2e année
Ottawa-Carleton
Catholic School Board

Changes in 2020

In the year 2020, I will be 28 years old. At that time, many things will be changed. For example:

1) Technological advancement:
   People will work with computers at home instead of going to work in the office.
   People will order grocery food and books through Internet shopping lists.
   People will see each other on the screen when they talk to each other on the phone.
   More new words are going to be in the computer dictionary.

2) More immigrants will come to Ontario:
   More job openings attract people around the world to come to Ontario.
   More houses, cars, schools, teachers, doctors, nurses, daycare centres, parks, stores, clothing, and other things will be needed for the newcomers.

3) More tourists in Ontario:
   As a tourist guide, I will take visitors around Ontario for beautiful sightseeings. I will arrange interesting tours and let people know more about Ontario as much as I can.

229

Grade 2 / 2ᵉ année
Central Montessori Schools
North York

Amanda Tam

When I Grow Up

Hello!! I am Julie Bédard. I am seven years old. I love dogs. In the year 2020 I think life will be hard. I am going to be a farmer/pilot. The way I am going to help the environment is I will grow trees. Which makes more oxygen for us to breathe. In the year 2020 if there is any garbage on the ground I will pick it up. In the year 2020 there could be a button in the kitchen, then you type the number in and you would get what you wanted. I would use my cattle to plow the field. And my horses. I would not use toxic products. In the year 2020 I will want to be a child. In the year 2020 I think it will be great!! And I think life will be great!!

Julia Bédard

Grade 2 / 2ᵉ année
Glebe Montessori School
Ottawa

230

Freedom

I live in Oakville. Oakville is in Ontario. In 20 years I think everything will be free and they will build more white houses so we could all live in one. We could take a private jet everywhere and the stores would change. And we could swim with a cat and dog and extinct animals would be on earth again. And the beach would have a sun set and extinct animals could live with you. The snow leprd would live with me and queen alexandra butterfly. And to see Jesus.

Samantha Pettinato

Grade 1 / 1ʳᵉ année
Halton Catholic District School Board

Millennium Meltdown

Grade 9 / 9e année
Toronto Catholic District School Board

Marielle Johnson

A Perspective of Our Future

As Scott Adams, writer for *Dilbert*, would say, "When I'm in the bookstore I always stop just long enough to de-alphabetize the books in the kids section, because the children are our future, which can't possibly be a good thing, so I try to slow them down whenever I can."

I will be 35 when the year 2020 rolls around. Right now I'm thinking, "Whoa! 35! It's so far away." But it seems like just yesterday when I scraped my knee outside and ran to my Mom with tears in my eyes asking for a Band-Aid. So I guess it won't be long until 35. I just wonder what it will be like. Will it be the same as it is now? Will technology turn the world upside-down? Will I even be alive in 2020? I can't answer this… but I have no choice, it's been assigned and I must complete it.

When I was smaller I had this *crazy* thought that by the year 1999 the earth would be destroyed and mankind would be no more. Well, it's 1999 and we are still alive. I also had this other *crazy* thought that in the year 2000 we would all be driving hover crafts, wearing shiny space suits, live in homes like the Jetsons (where you have no idea what's underneath those clouds under their home), and would have robots completing our daily chores and tending to our every need. I realized that by the year 2000 we all are going to be exactly the same as we are now. Trying so hard to find cures for many diseases, we will still be those frantic citizens with the same problems that we had the year before.

I believe that it will become a better world and people will be judged only by who they are, not what they look like. Maybe we'll find cures for these horrible diseases and it could be a possibility that people will be friendlier instead of being harsh and nasty towards others whom they dislike, which probably causes those bullies to begin a crime-filled life. At least that's what I hope will happen.

Cloning will be a major part in technology, but it will eventually become a terrible thing. Once we begin to clone humans it will take away our personality, our (details on our bodies) such as scars or marks, that we call our own, would be insignificant. Having so many of the same people/animals traipsing around the world would become dull. And if almost everyone had themselves cloned, the world population would literally double! The people with identical twins must be upset about this, but I won't get into that.

I am a child of today, who will probably become a woman of the future. I plan on completing high school, going to university, then becoming a writer, director or something that has to do with film and theatre. (But not acting.) I hope to get married but I'm not so sure about kids. If I do have children they will probably have to do an essay on what it would be like in the year 2050.

Our future lawyers, actors and prison dwellers are the children today. It seems to me that some of our children today are indolent and neglectful, but who knows, maybe they'll smarten up. Maybe they won't become the stereotyped teenager who smokes, swears and does horribly in school.

I really do hope that the world won't still be a sullen and unhappy place like it is now with all of the problems we have. It might become that "Jetsons" future I talked about, but maybe not. Who am I to tell you the perspective of our future?

Tara Urquhart   Grade 8 / 8e année

Off to a Great Start

As I sit in my desk and imagine what Ontario will be like in the year 2020, this picture comes to mind. I will be thirty-three and an organic farmer. Trees will line each farm and I'll pick up the last week's paper to find out that the world has made peace. Herbicides and pesticides have been replaced with ladybugs and people. This creates more jobs. It also makes Ontario a healthier place to live.

As I read on in my newspaper, I see that the hog business is booming and the loonie has been the same value as the American dollar for three years.

The next day, the paper boy rides by on his bike. I wave to him and he waves back. I go and pick up the paper. Then I read that Ontario has set a record of no crimes in a year. Poverty has gone down to zero percent in the last two years and the cure for AIDS and cancer has been discovered. Also chicken pox has been wiped out completely. The neighbour's kids come over and ask if they may swim in my pond. I smile and nod my head yes. These kids are the future generation and they're off to a great start.

233

Grade 6 / 6e année
Bluewater District School Board

Christine Clifford

Bio Dome

Welcome to Technorama #1A in 2020. All of Ontario has been divided into self-sufficient communities, each surrounded by a climate-controlled biodome. This community floats in the sky to save space. Other communities are on the ground, such as Toronto. Technorama #1A is the sister city to Toronto and the Toronto Space Port is contained within it. A small square opening in the biodome allows the aircrafts to enter the city. The biodome helps to increase agricultural production by controlling the weather within the sphere. The buildings in our community are very unique. Instead of many small food or clothing stores we have food central and fashion central. These buildings are tall and narrow so that they do not take up a lot of space. The average family lives in a condominium complex. Each complex houses 25 families. Richer families live in small domeshaped homes.

Everything needed for life is contained within the dome. Trees for producing oxygen, a farm for growing food, several stores, and a place of worship. The place of worship is non-denominational, containing (among others) churches, synagogues, and mosques. The school contains an Elementary School, High School, College, University, and Finishing School. The people and animals are not to scale so that they are more easily seen by the human eye. The actual size of the people would be about 100th of the size of the ones shown in our model. The rulers on the side of the biodome are to show antsize fluctuations that may happen within the sphere.

Almighty God, we ask you to bless our community
  Technorama #1A
We ask you to live among us and help us in our
  daily tasks
To make us better people and help us to be good
Everlasting God who created the earth help us to
  keep the earth clean
All powerful God who created people help us to
  treat others as we would like to be treated.
We ask from you, our Loving Parent
Yours sincerely,
The people of community Technorama #1A

234

235

Alanna Charles
Stephanie DiGiuseppe
Alexis Carere
A. Mathews
Adrienne O'Connor

Grade 8 / 8ᵉ année
Toronto Catholic
District School Board

David DiGiuseppe

Grade 4 / 4ᵉ année

Panorama 2020: The Domains of Man

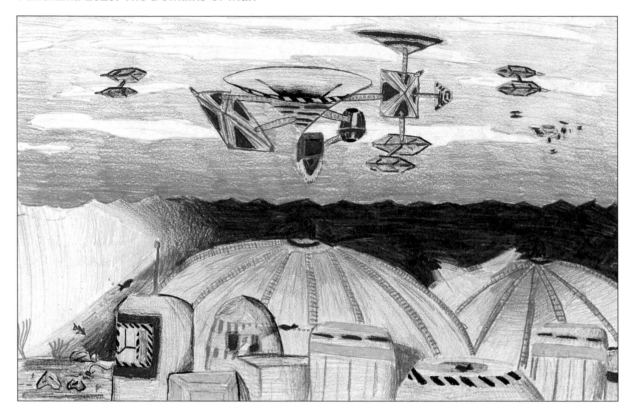

236

The sparkle of water, the sprinkle of space, these are the domains of man. In space an interplanetary network linking Mars, Earth and the power of the Moon unites in the discovery of inter-spacial technology. Man has ventured to the outer limits of our galaxy.

In the deep, dark depths of the ocean, bright lights from a massive sea vessel shimmer across the steel plating of the Pacific's breathtaking underwater city. The glowing lights fill the darkness with the ability to see.

Ontario and the world are united in peace, hoping for a future for our children. The world is known as Armistice, handpicked from the dictionary for its meaning: a stop in fighting by agreement on all sides. Our peace headquarters would be located in a huge garden filled with wild flowers walling their way around a crisp pond filled with all kinds of life. With our resources back to peak, man has achieved more than ever dreamed possible.

Unlike most people, I would not be a Supreme being but a civilian, a human helping humanity. Instead of mining the world to exhaustion, we recycle the metal for use in healthcare or transportation.

My vision is a world of peace, harmony and technology. We have saved our environment; that's what makes me proud. In my world money doesn't exist, you don't favor the rich and spit on the poor. You buy things for credits. All people are given the same amount of credits whether they are doctors or gas pumpers. Credits pay for items you wish to have. All jobs are important and they all must be completed efficiently.

Our flag has the red sides of Canada, the stars of the U.S., and an image of our world with the heart we share. We have come a long way and we'll keep on going. We have worked hard since the beginning of time, and we will continue our efforts to allow our way of life to survive. So in the sparkle of water or the sprinkle of space, we live *as* the domains of man.

237

Grade 7 / 7e année
Bluewater District School Board

Gordie Weppler

Peace & Love

I want there to be lots of trees in the year 2020.
I will help do that by planting lots of trees now.
I can help by not polluting the water.
I can help clean the air by not using so much hairspray, and by not using your car when you don't need to.
I can help to end racism by playing and working with all types of people.
That is how I will help to realize my vision of Ontario in the year 2020.

238

My Ontario 2020 Story

A, B, C.
One, two, three.
This is what I want my Ontario to be.
I want there to be more trees for the birds and me.
I want cleaner water for us to drink, and the fish to live in.
If we don't clean our water now, can you imagine how dirty it will be in the year 2020?
I want cleaner air for people to breathe so we don't get sick. I want the buildings and the factories not to have so much pollution coming from the smokestacks.
In the year 2020 I want all the people in Ontario to get along and to me that means no racism. Nobody will make fun of the colour of your skin, your religion or what country you come from.
A, B, C, that is what I want my Ontario to be.

Samantha Di Santo

Grade 3 / 3e année
Toronto Catholic District School Board

It Will Be Interesting

In the year 2020 I will be 30 years old. I would be having children soon or have had them already. I would want my children to live a long, healthy life. And live in a safe place.

In the year 2020 I hope that there won't be so much pollution. Maybe cars would run on something other than gas, like water. And maybe all garbage would disintegrate within two to three weeks. I don't know exactly how there will be less pollution, but there will *have* to be less, for us all to survive on earth.

I think that everybody might have their own web site with information on them. Maybe instead of going to school, children would go on-line. And instead of going into a chat room, you would go in a schoolroom.

I hope that in the future there is a new fun way of transportation. Also it would be cool if kids could take the driving test at an earlier age. And if they passed they could start driving right away.

I think that in the new millennium there will be more kinds of species, like cross species. I would like a cross species of a cat and dog.

I think it will be interesting to see Ontario in the year 2020!

239

Grade 5 / 5ᵉ année
Peel District School Board

Jessica Roberts

Hovercrafts and Other Things

In the year 2020, the biggest thing I hope is that there will be less pollution. Cars would run on air and be called hovercrafts. Hovercrafts would have scanners that could tell if you were drinking and wouldn't let you drive if you were. My car would be able to give me directions if I got lost and tell me how long it would take me to get somewhere. More people would use bicycles, rollerblades and walking or other ways to get around. Everyone would have to recycle and compost, this would be the law. I would plant trees at my home and people wouldn't be allowed to cut down trees for no reason. If they did cut down trees, then they would have to plant some more. I imagine a laser machine used to get rid of garbage. I see people using less chemicals, like using butter instead of Pam. The laws would be stricter about smoke coming out of factories.

I also see that there would be more things for kids and teenagers to do, like clubs and community centres. I think this would help them to keep busy and stay out of trouble. More things should be free for kids to do, like sports. Kids should be taught not to be prejudiced.

Computers would be everywhere. I would have a robot run by a computer. It would help me get dressed, help me with my work and my kids with their homework and clean my house. All phones would be video phones, and you could always see who you were talking to. My computer would be an alarm clock and it would wake me up by saying: "C'mon, lazybones, time to get up, Cailyn get out of bed!" It would keep doing this until I got up. My kids would be able to learn their schoolwork at home by using the computer. It would be the law that even poor kids had to have computers too, so they could learn the same things as everyone else. Everyone would be taught how to use a computer.

Everyone should know some French.

There should be no guns allowed, so people don't get killed.

Cailyn Edwards

Grade 3 / 3ᵉ année
Upper Canada District School Board

How to Make My Dream Come True

I had this dream that I was in the year 2020. Ontario was the most beautiful place on earth. The lakes were clear as glass; pebbles sparkled from the bottom of the lakes. Wildlife paused to drink along the peaceful rivers. People were healthy and strong because the water did not contain any bacteria or disease-causing germs.

There was no crime in Ontario. If someone committed a crime, he or she was sent to an island far, far away and dealt with severely.

Ontario had discovered a cure for all types of cancer! People were treated with this cure and overcame their sickness. This meant that less people got sick and more people stayed healthy and enjoyed life.

There was no pollution in Ontario because people had the courtesy to put garbage in garbage cans! They all cared about a safe and clean environment. Because of this there were fewer sicknesses and bacterial infections.

Everyone cared about the wildlife and didn't harm their habitat. They let nature take its course without affecting it in any way.

I also dreamt that people in Ontario hospitals were well taken care of. They got all the help they needed when they were ill and tired.

As you can see, the Ontario of my dreams, in the year 2020, was a beautiful, gorgeous and precious sight.

To make my dream come true, I will do many things. I will get people to sign petitions to keep the environment clean. I will also encourage them to volunteer their time and clean the subdivision in which they live. I will raise money to find a cure for cancer by running across Ontario. I will make speeches to fellow Ontarians about the pollution today and how we can stop it from being an issue in later years. I will hire the best police officers in Ontario to make sure everyone else feels safe. I will also talk to people about animals and how our wildlife depends on the environment as much as we depend on it.

All of these things require a lot of effort and energy. I know I will succeed because hard work equals success.

Catherine Canapini

Grade 6 / 6ᵉ année
Durham Catholic District School Board

241

Brochure

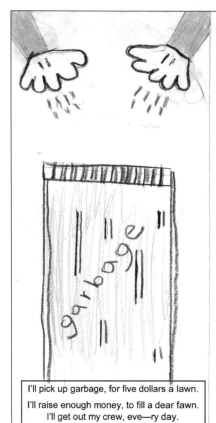

I'll pick up garbage, for five dollars a lawn.

I'll raise enough money, to fill a dear fawn.
I'll get out my crew, eve—ry day.

Together, we'll sweep all the garbage away.

MY WORLD IN 2020

We'll take all of our money,

and buy lots of clothes.

Blue shirts, new shirts,

ones the colour of your nose.

We'll take all of our clothes,

and give them to the poor.

we'll ship clothes across Ontario,

so that the people might have more.

Eryn Campbell

Grade 3 / 3e année
Durham Catholic District School Board

Pass the Torch

In 2020 we each know,
Ontario will continue to boast.
Because today, we put our toil,
To where it matters most.
Into issues of importance,
That affect each and everyone.
So that in the future, we will pass the torch,
Onto our daughter and our son.

Our province will remain,
Quite a gorgeous place.
Because each and everyone tries,
To put litter in its place.
The water and the lakes,
We'll continue to keep clear.
Because a healthy environment,
Is my vision for that year.

My province it will offer,
To everyone within.
A place where we feel safe,
Despite the colour of our skin.
A home to grow and live life well,
With family and friends.
To share our rich Ontario,
With those of other lands.

A good education will be there,
To all within our schools.
So we can grow and learn to be,
Adults with the tools.
To govern and to rule our land,
With fairness and with heart.
And each of us will stand with pride,
Because we know we've done our part.

243

Grade 6 / 6ᵉ année
Peterborough Victoria Northumberland
and Clarington Catholic
District School Board

Jenna O'Connor

My Vision of Ontario in 2020!

244

I learned about this contest through my teacher Mrs. Pridham. I decided that I would like to enter. Now I know that many of you were probably thinking that I would draw flying spaceships and all, but I chose to look upon it another way. I chose to draw pictures about what I would like to see happen and what I would like to have stay. I will tell you about what all my little drawings are about.

I will start by describing the picture about the computer. What I am saying here is that I would like to still have the Internet when I am older and have children. I think that the Net has many informative things on it. One thing I would like to have changed would definitely be what goes on the Internet though. I really hope that in the future there won't be anything about how to make bombs and such. I would like things about my province, explorers, and much more.

The next picture I will describe is the one with the garbage can and the person. This picture is about what I would like changed. I wish that in the future, Ontario will be free of litter. I also hope that people will care about the environment and take the time to just put their trash in the garbage can. This is something I would really like changed.

Thirdly, I will tell you about the two pictures involving sports. I know that I love sports and I hope that when I have kids, they will too. Playing sports is a great pleasure and I hope that in the future, Ontario will still have the freedom to play the sports they love. That is what those pictures are about.

Lastly, I will describe what the picture is about involving the drugs. I am saying that I would like it if there were no street drugs available in the future. I would also like it if there were no cigarettes available either. I also hope that people won't misuse their medication or take advantage of Tylenol or other painkillers. I would like that to happen. I will personally contribute to making my visions a reality by not doing drugs, playing sports, not littering, and by going on the Internet.

I think Ontario will be great in the year 2020. I definitely look forward to the future and hope that my visions will come true. Ontario is part of Canada, which is a free country, but there is no other province I would rather live in than here in Ontario!

245

Grade 6 / 6ᵉ année
York Region District School Board

Krista Montgomery

Wishes from a Kindergarten Class

"When I grow up, I want my *Ontario* to be clean. I want the rubbish to be picked up." *Druceilla*

"I want the people to love each other and like each other a lot." *Shalina*

"When I grow up, I want my *Ontario* to be safe; for you to be OK in your home." *Areag*

"I want to do lots of work and make it clean." *Tyronne*

"I want everyone to play safe and carefully. I don't want anyone to fight." *Victoria*

"I want the whole town to be nice and shiny and I want everyone to play safe." *Ryan*

"I want everybody to share." *Yuvraj*

"I want the animals to be safe and I want to see the animals really eat and share with the food; that the animals don't grab." *Pardeep*

"My *Ontario* is gonna be clean, clean, clean. We can work, get money, go to school, and buy food from the store." *Natasha*

"My *Ontario* is going to be big." *Kizanee*

"I want my *Ontario* to be clean. I'm going to pick up a garage bag and go outside." *Aaron*

"I want Ontario to look happy and no one to be mad." *Victoria*

"I will clean Ontario and pick up garbage." *Gurpal*

"Some people are gonna be white, some people are gonna be black and some people are gonna be brown." *Druceilla*

"We want them to like each other and love each other and be friends." *Shalina*

246

Grade K / Maternelle
Peel District School Board

Buildings of the Future

Grade 8 / 8ᵉ année
Peel District School Board

Jaspreet Sandhu

247

248

Millennium Ontario

Upper Ca-nada in central land sing
mil-len-nium hand-in-hand.

Chorus
Mil-len-nium, mil-len-nium, it's coming oh
so fast.
Mil-len-nium, mil-len-nium, 1990's in the
past.
On-ta-rio, On-ta-rio, oh what will you
become?
On-ta-rio, On-ta-rio, true as the tril-li-um.

Ma-chines and ro-bots and fan-cy cars.
Will the as-tro-nauts land on Mars?
20-20 a special year.
It's a new mil-len-nium don't you fear.

Chorus
Technicolours in the sky.
Robotic birds are flying by.
Electronic people in the street.
All the houses built of pure concrete.
Mil-len-nium, On-ta-rio say good-bye to the
past.

Elaine Anselmi

Grade 6 / 6ᵉ année
Toronto District School Board

My Thoughts about 2020

What would Ontario look like in the year 2020? I think it wouldn't look that different, just a little more details in places like Toronto would have a lot more detail, like floating cars or more stores and restaurants to go to. There will be many places to have fun like giant amusement parks. In my town, Orangeville, we have a main street called Broadway. I think that Broadway is going to be like the Broadway that's in New York.City.

Would construction of buildings be as difficult? No, it wouldn't be as difficult because the cities would have improved machines to build buildings faster and easier. Would these machines work like robots? These machines wouldn't work like robots because men and women construction workers would be controlling these machines.

My hopes and dreams for the year 2020 is for no homeless people, no criminals, and definitely no hunger. I hope that things get better in the year 2020. If things don't get better in the year 2020, I will be there trying my best to make things better.

Thank you for listening to my thoughts about the year 2020.

250

Tarah Casole-Buchanan

Grade 4 / 4e année
Dufferin-Peel Catholic
District School Board

Description of What I Would Like to See...

Simon is a 19-year-old student at Lucy McCormick School in Toronto. He has a developmental disability and cerebral palsy. He communicates using a voice output device, by pointing, and by indicating "yes" or "no" by nodding or shaking his head. He loves the school program and is eager to engage in learning activities and tasks that challenge him to use his hands for purposeful work, and to keep up his walking skills. When he leaves school next year there are presently very few programs to help him maintain active and purposeful daily work. His choices here indicate that he would like to have this available to him even after school.

251

Ungraded Senior Class for Students with Developmental Disabilities Toronto District School Board

Simon Dell

The Dream that Changed the Future

One dark and extremely stormy night in Toronto, everything was silent, except the noise of the thunder. I couldn't get any sleep because I was really scared by the winter storm. My dad tried many things to get me asleep, but nothing seemed to work.

"Look on the bright side, Bilal, there are many people on the street who have no homes to sleep, and they're getting soaked by the rain, imagine how they feel," my dad said.

I was feeling really sorry for them. That night I had a dream that changed my life forever.

I dreamt that I was one of thousands of homeless people on the street. In my dream I had nowhere to go, and nothing to eat. I was halfway from freezing to death.

I woke up exactly at 6:43 a.m. because of one loud noise created by the thunder. The rest of the morning I stayed awake listening to the latest news on the winter storm.

Later on that day, I told my dad all about what I had dreamt. My dad was really worried about me, and he felt sorry that he had ever mentioned to look on the bright side.

The next day I went outside to give some change to some of the homeless people. Since that day I always gave them money or gave them some food to eat. Soon the news spread everywhere, I was on the front page of a weekly newspaper for spending about one third of my allowance on homeless people.

I continued to do this until I thought of just doing one thing that will help the people with no homes forever, by that time I was an adult, earning a lot of money.

With all the money I had saved up, I decided to open a school, not just any school, but a school just for homeless people. With the help of the government, I got all the homeless people in Ontario to come to my school. I hired many teachers. They all educated the homeless people and got them jobs, so they buy or rent a place to live.

My plan was a success, by the year 2020 there weren't any more homeless people in all of Ontario!

252

Bilal Haque

Grade 5 / 5e année
Toronto District School Board

Communiquer avec les martiens

Moi, Evelyne, une Ontarienne de l'an 2020,
J'ai inventé un moyen de communiquer avec les martiens.

Un jour, ils sont venus sur terre
Avec leur grosse soucoupe de verre.
Nous étions tous très fiers
Qu'ils fassent partie de notre univers.

Les martiens sont restés un mois,
Et nous ont appris à mieux s'occuper de nos forêts et nos bois.
Ils se sont fait un petit ami, un chiwawa
Qu'ils ont nommé Pitawa.

Ils nous ont appris à communiquer avec les animaux
Ils nous ont appris à respecter notre eau.
Ils ont dépollué l'air, Ha, que le ciel était beau!

Ils sont partis et avec tristesse,
En nous donnant tous de grosses caresses.
Le coeur lourd de laisser leurs amis terrestres,
En espérant un jour de revenir avec allégresse.

253

5e année / Grade 5
Conseil scolaire du district
catholique de l'Est Ontarien

Evelyne Sirois-Carey

Future Findings

The eye of future findings
Blinks to twenty years ahead
To majestic, proud Ontario
When the sun's first light is shed

The yellow shafts spear downward
Through a canopy of green
Onto ribbons of pure water
Staining rocks with diamond sheen

The stillness is not broken
With the quarreling of races
But the peace is built on tolerance
The warmth of different faces

And sheltered in the reaches
Of the proud land and its past
I smile for our Ontario
And enlightenment at last

Twenty years has blessed us
With the knowledge we have sought
And fifty years, a hundred
Bring the happiness we've wrought

254

Mel Maltby

Grade 12 / 12e année
Algoma District School Board

What I Clearly See

Ontario 2020

Here is what I clearly see,
for the future, for you and me.
No more fighting or doing wrong,
instead we're all singing the world's cheerful song.
We all have new jobs, new clothes, and new shoes,
New candy, and chocolate, french fries, and stews.
Inventions are created, both new and old,
like TV's and telephones made of ten carot gold.
We all will obey, we all will love,
Just like the spirit that lives high above.
Ontario is safe, so unlock your doors,
We stopped all the fighting there are no more wars!

I will help by being cool,
always be good and stay in school.
I won't pollute but I will recycle,
I'll run, or walk, or bicycle.
I'll plant flowers and trees,
for the birds and for the bees,
so around they will fly,
up, up and away into the sky.
It is not hard what I will do,
so try it yourself, you can help too!

255

Grade 7 / 7ᵉ année
London District Catholic School Board

Ashley Thom

In 21 Years . . .

Tues., April 13th, 1999.

<u>Ontario's Future 2020</u>

In 21 years I am going to be a teacher. I think Ontario is going to look like a big jungle-gym because it will have alot of forests with slides, swings, monkey-bars, trampalines, and swimming pools. The cars would be different because all you would have to do is tell them where to go. They would have no steering wheels and they would be automatic. We would also have houses, roads, libraries, and planes. We will still have subways, trains, and Go trains. There would be alot more schools in Ontario where I would like to teach.

256

There would be stores except you will not have to bye the things in it, you can just take them. Ontario will smell like flowers all the time and it will always be spring or summer because there will never be anymore winters. There will always be beautiful green grass with the prettiest most wonderful flowers with big huge meadows, prairies, fields and mountains. There will be so many animals. The birds would always be singing. There would be alot of water and big huge bridges to help us travel throughout Ontario.

Rachel De Clavasio

Grade 2 / 2e année
Halton Catholic District School Board

257

L'avenir de l'Ontario

Le Canada est un peu plus petit qu'il ne l'était en 1999 car les trois lunes ont brassé les marées. L'eau a inondé un quart du Canada. La superficie a changé mais la renommée et la vie des gens sont restées intactes.

Un changement qui a eu lieu est l'aspect terrestre du Canada. La végétation de l'Ontario est devenue tropicale. Les arbres sont énormes et procurent au Canada son économie dynamique. La pluie en Ontario est abondante et quand il y a du soleil, il fait chaud et parfois les gens sont forcés à prendre des siestes à cause de la chaleur intense. Les hivers, comme les étés, sont chauds mais le taux d'humidité est beaucoup plus élevé. Cela ne représente pas un problème car les manteaux typiques du 21ième siècle, fabriqués de différentes fibres plastiques, filtrent l'eau dans l'air en gardant le corps sec à une température idéale.

L'autre changement est la technologie. Le progrès est incroyable! Les maladies sont éliminées; cela n'est pas nouveau car ça fait au moins 10 ans qu'il n'y a aucune épidémie de virus ou de bactéries. Et pour cinq années d'affilée, la province de l'Ontario a été déclarée

«la plus en forme de tout l'univers.» Le crime n'est plus un problème car les criminels ont tous été programmés de nouveau. Un type de lobotomie est exécuté sur les criminels ayant une nature violente. La partie de leur cerveau qui produit les images et l'envie de violence est enlevée. L'argent n'existe plus car un microprocesseur implanté dans le tissu de la main remplace l'argent en papier et les pièces d'argent. Aussi, ce microprocesseur remplace la carte d'identité, d'assurance et même la carte de santé. Un autre bénéfice de ce monde technologique est le voyage rapide. La plupart des maisons ont des plateaux qui rendent possible les voyages dans le passé et dans le futur.

Si une personne veut visiter sa mère avant son décès ou un oncle qu'elle ne voit jamais, cela est possible grâce à une courte randonnée dans le passé. Mais attention car la visite ne peut durer qu'une demi-heure. Si la visite dépasse cette durée, la personne risque d'être prise dans le passé. Le voyage par téléporteur dans les différents pays est plus sécuritaire et est disponible au bureau d'agence de voyages. Ce voyage ne coûte que 50 doplores (le nom pour le crédit). Une autre méthode pour voyager est par vaisseau. Les «vesyages» sont plus dispendieux mais l'expérience est inoubliable. Je recommande fortement d'aller à Dakput dans la constellation Karlut. Cette planète est belle mais pas aussi belle que notre Ontario, un endroit d'élégance réelle et de richesses naturelles.

Pendant longtemps, notre société a eu peur de la technologie et de la venue du nouveau millénaire. Elle pensait que notre planète serait détruite mais le contraire est survenu. La société se réjouit dans le bonheur qui est la vie et n'a plus peur de l'avenir. Les gens savent que la vie va finir, quand elle va finir et c'est l'attitude de tout le monde, pas seulement des Ontariens et Ontariennes. Peut-être cette nouvelle attitude provient de l'éducation mondiale. Par cela je veux dire que tous les gens sont éduqués. En plus d'être intelligents, ils sont proches de leurs voisins et voisines. Tout le monde se réunit à dix-huit heures pour regarder le coucher du soleil et de la lune et le lever des deux lunes nocturnes. L'atmosphère n'est plus polluée car les automobiles utilisent l'herbe comme carburant et il n'existe plus d'industries polluantes.

Depuis mon succès sur la scène et avec mes ventes de livres, je suis une philanthrope pour plusieurs groupes. J'appuie beaucoup l'industrie des sciences et des avances technologiques mais je dois avouer que je ne partage pas l'idée de mes confrères et consoeurs en ce qui concerne la technologie, elle ne me fait pas peur. Je suis d'accord avec certains aspects des sciences mais, quant au clonage et à la lobotomie, je suis en désaccord avec ces méthodes. J'essaie de me convaincre que c'est pour l'avenir de notre planète et, si la technologie n'était pas arrivée, notre planète serait détruite par notre pollution.

Côté familial, j'ai deux filles et deux garçons qui sont entièrement dévoués aux sciences. Mon aînée apprend la médecine à l'école secondaire et mes trois plus jeunes apprennent les stratégies et les concepts de la technologie. Évidemment, l'éducation en Ontario s'est énormément améliorée et est très avancée. Les enfants font leur choix de carrière très jeunes. Cela les prépare pour leur vie future. Lorsqu'il y a des conférences au sujet de l'industrie et du gouvernement au Canada et en Europe, je suis toujours la première appelée grâce à ma vaste connaissance de langues. Mes livres historiques donnent aux gens une certaine nostalgie de ne pas avoir connu un monde qui n'existe plus. L'industrie des films et des théâtres donne l'occasion aux gens de faire autre chose que les drogues du 20ième siècle. Les oeuvres de mon choix sont écrites avant le 20ième siècle, avant la corruption et le malheur. J'essaie de faire ressortir la vie et d'obtenir une réaction positive de la société, pour les faire penser, et pour développer leur imagination et aussi pour leur apprendre qu'ils sont chanceux d'avoir une bonne vie, d'avoir une vie, et d'être aimés. Il en est de même pour mes toiles d'art et mes histoires.

Je trouve que j'ai accompli beaucoup pour ma planète. J'ai mis au monde quatre enfants qui feront une différence. Mon argent a aidé l'évolution de la planète et de la société et j'ai fait réagir le monde entier par mes contes et mes pièces. Je suis finalement contente et si je devais mourir demain, je n'en serais pas enragée ou attristée car tout ce que je voulais faire a été accompli. J'ai toujours voulu laisser ma marque et je l'ai laissée dans ce monde, sur cette planète, dans cette province qu'on appelle l'Ontario.

259

12e année / Grade 12
Conseil scolaire du district du
Nord-Est de l'Ontario

Cristiane Peever

**Départ vers
le futur!**

260

Marie-Josée Laviolette

8e année / Grade 8
Conseil des écoles publiques de
l'Est de l'Ontario

Shaping the Future Together

Grade 6 / 6e année   **Ashley Anselmo**

261

Magnificent Ontario: The International Hot-Spot

I took a trip recently. My parents and I travelled from our home in a small town in Northern Ontario to one of the big Southern Ontario cities. As we drove along the highway, I marvelled at the beauty in the ever-changing scenery. My parents were deep in conversation about the fate of our province and, as I listened to the dooms of education, health care, and our natural resources, I drifted into a daydream of what my Ontario will be like in the future, in the year 2020.

I have lived in Ontario all my life. I've always enjoyed the many things Ontario has to offer: its history, its beauty, and, of course, its friendly people. When I think of the future I see Ontario remaining as prosperous as it is today, but in a very different way.

There has been much fretting over the fate of Ontario. We have seen the possibility of creating two provinces, Northern and Southern Ontario, to better suit the needs of people. Northern Ontario is slowly losing its two main resources, mining and forestry. This is a cause for great concern. What will happen to Ontario when these resources are gone? Prophecies of doom and gloom seem to surround us. But I have a much greater vision for Ontario in the year 2020.

It does seem sad that the industries that once shaped most of our province, mining and forestry, will no longer exist. However, imagine the possibilities to come from molding the vast amount of land into a brand new industry — tourism. Ontario will become the new hot spot for people from all over the world. Millions will flock to be in the Great Scenic North.

Ontario's resorts will offer every activity anyone could ever want. In the winter there will be skiing, sledding, snowmobiling, snowshoeing, hunting, ice-fishing, skating, polar dips, and hockey. In the summer, swimming, water-skiing, fishing, boating, sailing, soccer, and just lazing around enjoying the beautiful temperatures.

And there would always be the historical aspects of Ontario's resorts: the fact that they all would be built on the grounds of an old mining community. A visitor to a resort could take a tour in an old abandoned mine and learn how the miners of the old days lived.

What a revenue these resorts would create for Ontario and Canada itself. Thousands of jobs would be created — people to run the hotels, the events, the transportation, the restaurants. And there may not be just fancy resorts for people to travel to. Ontario is well known for its beautiful campgrounds and parks. Perhaps there would be a world-renowned camp for children to go to with each camp session revolving around the sports of that season. The possibilities are endless.

When I return from university with my Public Relations degree, I could travel the world promoting the magnificent Ontario Resorts. I would make it known that Ontario is the place for all ages and interests.

As I continue to gaze out the window I snap out of my daydream filled with hope for the future of my province. My mind begins to wander again, but this time it is to envision the grand buildings that will line this highway in the not-so-distant future. Then I begin to envision my own future — maybe an exclusive resort of my own where all the most famous Hollywood actors will stay. Hey, I'd like a little piece of the prosperity for myself.

Mary-Katherine McMillan

OAC
Northeastern Catholic
District School Board

The Planets Are Connected by Ladders in 2020

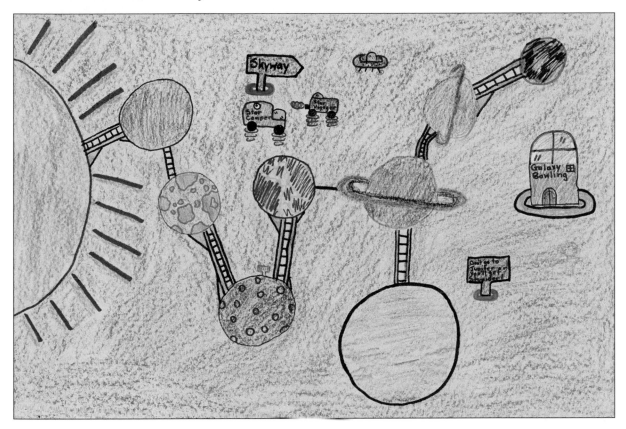

Grade 4 / 4ᵉ année
Superior North Catholic District School Board

Tara Allaire

264

Aliens Will Visit Ontario

There will be a slide down to earth and there will be ladders to go back to space. Kids' clothes will have their school things on them. The school will change and the aliens will visit Ontario. There will be less school and I will be famous. There will be a cure for cancer.

Krista Harvey

Grade 2 / 2ᵉ année
Superior North Catholic
District School Board

My Ontario on April 21, 2020

April 21st, 2020 – Ontario has become one of the most developed places in the world. The provincial debt is almost nil, thanks to the Money Management Act. This act produced more jobs, cut taxes, put more money into healthcare and education, and made the Canadian dollar worth twice as much as the American dollar.

Crime has dropped by 75%. This is because the government has gotten tougher on criminals. Technology has improved so much that if you commit a crime there is a 99% chance that you will be found by satellites located throughout space.

Tobacco has become prohibited. There were a few protests but they gradually died down.

Cars that run on gasoline have become "extinct." Only a few are left in antique stores. The rest have been recycled and have been made into other metal things. There are plastic cars that run on electricity, batteries and solar power. Flying cars are a long way off, but people say they should be in the market within 10 years.

In the home there are a few things that have become "extinct." Among these are the standard dishwasher, washer and stove. The microwave has taken the place of the stove and oven. Scientists have discovered a way to clean things without water.

In fashion, **JEANS STILL RULE!** Bellbottoms and flares are flops right now, and a new type of jeans are in style. They have been cut in a zigzag fashion at the leg bottoms and are given the appropriate name, Zigzags.

The average person's income is between $150,000 to $200,000. Remember though, that things cost more. A regular box of Kraft Dinner costs $4.99. That is one of the few problems that still exist.

AIDS and HIV have become "extinct" like smallpox. Treatments have eliminated most diseases. Cancer is treated by one injection.

As a contribution to our future, I will try to be a politician and try to convince the government to understand that they need to manage their money better. I want to invent things that will save the people and the government money, like waterless dishwashers.

If everyone pitches in, the year 2020 will become one of the best years in the history of mankind.

Grade 8 / 8e année

Kathy Kirkman

The Year 2020 — Dean's Solar Dream House

My year 2020 Dream House is a very cost-efficient house. It has many features that keep costs down on all kinds of things. The price starts at about five hundred thousand dollars. That may seem extravagant but in the long term this house will pay for itself.

My house is constructed out of three-inch glass, metal, and non-meltable plastics. The insulation is foam and can be put in tight spaces, which is perfect for a glass house. The glass is strong enough to be hit by three-hundred-mile-an-hour winds. The steel is very strong. The plastic is durable but inexpensive, and it really gives this house an edge.

The house has two floors and a basement which runs the full length of the house. There is a family room with a big screen television, a games room, and an insulated cold room in the basement for storing food.

On the main floor there are two bathrooms with walk-in showers, pedestal sinks, and toilets. All fixtures are water conservation units. There is a large kitchen with remote-controlled, energy-efficient appliances. Other rooms on this floor include a large living room and a super high-tech computer room.

The second floor has five bedrooms. Four of them are normal-sized bedrooms but the fifth is the master bedroom. It has a large en suite bathroom. The entire upstairs has cathedral ceilings which add to the architectural appeal of this house.

At the back of this house there is a deck that runs the full length of the house. It is made of pressure-treated, plastic-covered wood. There is an in-ground pool, a fifteen-person hot tub, and a small wading pool. The front of the house has a veranda with a railing and entry to the front of the house.

At the side of the house there is a five-car garage with remote-controlled garage door opener. The roof of the house has solar collector panels. The roof and walls are super-insulated to prevent heat loss. There are also wind generators at the rear of the property. There is an in-ground heat pump system as a backup for the heating system and to cool the house in the summer. Grey water is collected via a system of pipes and used to water lawns and gardens. The grounds surrounding the house will have many trees to assist with shade and to have a cooling effect for the house.

It is my dream to become an architect. I would design and build such a house by the year 2020.

267

Sarah Loback

Grade 11 / 11ᵉ année
Renfrew County District School Board

The Government Project 2020

Ontario so grand and strong
Home to an ever-growing throng
Thousands of inhabitants
Within your borders
Etching out their future
In pursuit of honours.

Your ribbons of highway
Carry us on
To factories and offices
Schools and beyond
Over rolling hills and Precambrian shield,
Farmland and mines with bounteous yields.

Many new opportunities for those who strive
Equipped with education
And inherent drive
All helping to contribute and give more
To this great province we care for.

We play in your green fields
Saved from decay
We swim in your crystal waters
Enjoying the day.
We walk on your streets
Free from worry,
Escaping from stress,
Pressures and hurry.

Our policies and standards
Have kept you strong
Clean and safe
Ensuring full, long
And prosperous lives
We can be proud of.
We look to the future
With prospect and love.

Ontario so grand and strong
My hope, my dream, my vision, my home.

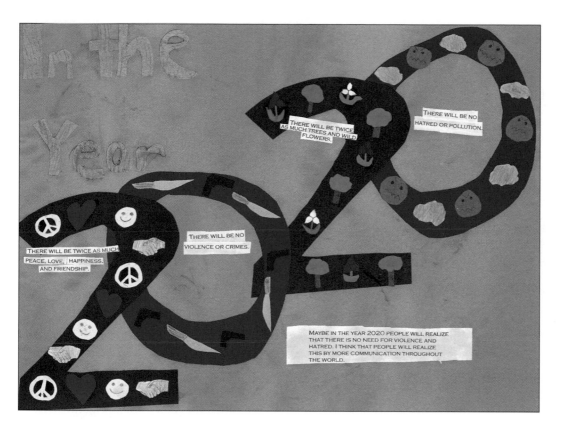

In the Year 2020

There will be twice as much
peace, love, happiness,
and friendship.

There will be no
violence or crimes.

There will be twice
as much trees and wild
flowers.

There will be no
hatred or pollution.

Maybe in the year 2020 people will realize
that there is no need for violence and
hatred. I think that people will realize
this by more communication throughout
the world.

Jenny Homebrook

Grade 5 / 5ᵉ année
Peel District School Board

270

The Best Place to Be

My Ontario! My Ontario;
The best place to be, there are houses and parks
And everything you need
So come down to Ontario,
And just remember this
My Ontario! My Ontario,
The best place to be.

Chuba

Grade 5 / 5e année
Peel District School Board

My Millennium Alphabet

What will happen after Y2K?
Will things change,
 will they stay the same?
What will be new?
Will people's impossible
 thoughts come true?

My millennium alphabet
 may be hullabaloo,
But it may come true
 in Malibu or Timbuktu
So listen up
 and see me through.

Here is what I think will
 happen…

A is for asteroids, will one ever hit?

B is for bicycles, the future mode of transit.

C is for computers, which will become much smaller.

D is for disease, will we all catch cholera?

E is for Earth, for which we must care.

F is for forecast, what can we do to prepare?

G is for glaciers, with warmth will they melt?

H is for houses, where we always have dwelt.

I is for improvement, which the world should achieve.

J is for junk food, will it become healthy, do you believe?

K is for keepsakes, the keys to the past.

L is for languages, will the old ones be outclassed?

M is for magic, will there be more secrets revealed?

N is for nuclear bombs, will life be like a minefield?

O is for organized and original, what the world should be like.

P is for Pluto, we're going to have to live there. Psyche!

Q is for queen, how long will she reign?

R is for recycling, let's use things again.

S is for school, with a new winter break.

T is for television, our lives it will take.

U is for universe, which we will explore.

V is for viruses, will there be more?

W is for women, the mothers of the land.

X is for x-ray, will technology expand?

Y is for yo-yo, will that toy return?

Z is for zodiac, from our future signs what will we learn?

So, that is what I think will happen after Y2K.
What do you think, and what would you say?

271

Grade 6 / 6ᵉ année
Toronto District School Board

Keiko Kataoka

Laurel Myers

Grade 3 / 3ᵉ année
Dufferin-Peel Catholic
District School Board

272

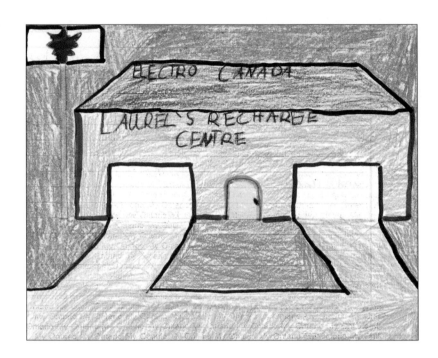

Dear Diary: August 10, 2020

Dear Diary,

Today is my twenty-ninth birthday. The time has gone by fast since we opened our recharge centre to help with pollution. Our daughter, Jessica, is in grade three and things are so different from when I was her age. We couldn't do anything without our home computer system. I just finished ordering groceries, making appointments, checking information at work and doing Jessica's homework all from home. Orangeville has doubled in size since I was eight and now there are lots of jobs, stores and recreation centres.

We went to Toronto and I thought that Lake Ontario looked dirtier than when I was small, but the air was cleaner because most of the new cars have electric engines.

Mom and Dad are retired now and in good health thankfully, because the hospitals are so busy with people their age. Mom and Dad call these people "baby boomers."

I have to end now because our new remote control vacuum just sent me a message that I have to pick up some socks in Jessica's room. How did we manage without these conveniences?

My Beautiful Ontario

In the year 2020 I will be the premier of Ontario. I have a plan to make Ontario beautiful. Everybody would start picking up trash. I would have more garbage cans around. When people go shopping they would have to bring their own containers. I would not allow people to kill animals just for fun. I would make forests for animals to live in. I would let people take pictures of the animals and they would love the animals and take care of them and their forest.

Awesome!

My Beautiful Ontario

In the year 2020 I will be the premier of Ontario. I have a plan to make Ontario beautiful. Everybody would start picking up trash. I would have more garbage cans around. When people go shopping they would have to bring their own containers. I would not allow people to kill animals →

by Lisa Black   Grd 2   St. Benedict

273

Grade 2 / 2ᵉ année
Dufferin-Peel Catholic
District School Board

Lisa Black

Things That Are Important

Year 2020

I'm 29 years old. My job will be an Animal Saver from hunters, because, killing animals is really really bad. I want all animals to be safe. Ontario will be a new province with all nice people. All the robbers will be in jail and there will not be any drugs. Nature will not be polluted from any cars. People could walk, ride bikes or go on the subway. It will be peacefull in all places in Ontario. No garbage thrown on the ground. The lake of Ontario will not have garbage These things are Important to Ontario

because it's a peacefull place. Well, thats all I could talk about. Bye!

Brenda Hoang

Grade 2 / 2e année
Toronto District School Board

274

Let's Put Our Minds Together

My Ontario

I think in the year 2020,
we will have invented plenty!

Now we have computers, pagers, T.Vs and cars,
telephones, airplanes, space exploration and bars.

In 2020 who knows what we'll make,
maybe cars that fly or self baking cake!

Also that year we could devise,
artificial seeing eyes!

In 2020 hopefully we'll clean up,
with no pollution or no dirty dump!

In the future we'll have easier lives,
with computerized houses and laser beam knives!

People could be living in space,
Mars or the moon would be a nice place!

But all these inventions aren't so "cool",
if war, world hunger and pollution are still the rule.

So lets put our minds together and think for a
of making the world better for everyone who bit,
lives on it!

Grade 6 / 6e année
Hamilton-Wentworth
District School Board

Carla Szwarz

Le futur est un mystère

Au temps quand ce sera l'année 2020
Il y aura beaucoup de possibilités

Tous les trains et les voitures au monde flotteront
C'est là, à la lune où nous tous voyagerons

Nous pourrons voir qui nous téléphonons c'est sûr
Et les télévisions seront accrochées aux murs

Il y aura une guérison pour le cancer
Et pour toujours seront finies les guerres

On utilisera l'empreinte de nos doigts
Car le monde aura de différentes lois

C'est vrai qu'il y aura des possibilités
Mais c'est vrai que des choses seront plus compliquées

De toujours vivre dans des dômes nous serons forcés
Car l'air et l'eau et la terre seront trop pollués

Pour tout le monde le futur est un mystère
Une chose est certaine ce ne sera pas comme hier

Brianne Chittle

8e année / Grade 8
Conseil scolaire du district des écoles
catholiques de Sud-Ouest de l'Ontario

Changements radicaux

L'Ontario en l'an 2020

R. Manitoba
c. Winnipeg

Baie d'Hudson

Baie James

Québec - Québec

Ontario

La glace a fondu et la baie James a débordé. Cette baie est devenue grosse comme la baie d'Hudson.

La ville en l'an 2020

Toronto

Ste - Marie

Embrun

Otawa

St-Guillaume

Russel

Montréal

boulevard Promenade

Le village d'Embrun va être deux fois plus gros qu'avant. Il pou On construira une autre école secondaire. Il va y avoir des parcs spéciaux pour les arbres et les animaux. La ville de Russell et d'Embrun va devenir une seule ville.

4ᵉ et 5ᵉ année / Grades 4 & 5
Conseil scolaire du district catholique
de l'Est Ontarien

Sonia Dignard

Est-ce que tu sais ce que l'Ontario va ressembler en 2020

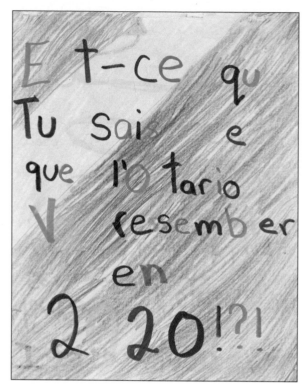

Ici en 2020 la forme de l'Ontario sera différente à celle d'aujourd'hui.

279

Voici la nourriture que nous mangerons en 2020!

L'Ontario en 2020 aura sûrement des différents animaux!

280

Stephanie Godin

4e année / Grade 4
Conseil scolaire du district catholique
de l'Est Ontarien

In My Vision...

Ontario will be very different in the year 2020. In my vision, there will be...

More people will be trying to save wildlife. We already know that there are many endangered species; some species only have about 500 of their kind left. I think the laws will be much stronger about killing animals. The laws about polluting the land and oceans will be much stronger too. Maybe instead of a 100 dollar fine for polluting, there will be a 500 dollar fine. Think about it, if you pollute the land, you're polluting the trees that help you to breathe.

Back in the 1800s, the money was worth more than it is today. For example, a pencil cost about a penny. I think that in the year 2020, money will be worth either a lot more (pencil=a penny) or a lot less (pencil=$20). Things like paper, pencils, and furniture might be more expensive, for trees are becoming endangered.

Food, food, food. Boy, in the year 2020, the food could even be different. There could be a drink — that actually tastes good — containing all of the food groups. Maybe everything will be packaged like TV dinners. Or maybe instead of people working in factories, robots will.

In order to make some of my visions become realities, I will try to research how to make different foods, and someday make a drink with all of the food groups. I will try to take a computer programming course (to make a robot). I will reduce, reuse, and recycle — and not pollute — now and when I grow up, and when I have children, I'll encourage them to save wildlife.

281

Grade 6 / 6e année
Avon Maitland District School Board

Meghan Burns

As Another Day Ends...

As another day ends, I make my way to the lobby of the twenty-eight-storey building that I work in in downtown Hamilton. The elevator has stopped five times already and will stop at least another five times, for it is 11:30 p.m. and everybody has the same thing in mind: time to go home! I work for the Medicinal Laboratories for Pharmacies of Ontario, or the M.L.P.O. building. For the last year I've been working on a project for the testing of a new medicine to improve one's level of energy that is supposed to be put out on the market next month. And I can't help but think that it is just another advancement towards the pill that will prolong young and healthy lifestyles, which seems to be on the minds of everybody these days. Ever since the cure for cancer has been discovered and practised, everybody is looking for something that will make them even healthier and younger. Nobody has time to take care of themselves so they turn to people like me to make their lives easier. Majority of people are working right out of their homes on their computers and they have

a tendency to do absolutely nothing with their free time. I love my job, but I don't love the reasons behind my work.

I step into a world of bright lights and to the sound of the high-speed trains two blocks away. The sky is brightly filled with beautiful stars; however, they are quite difficult to see with all of the streetlights and lights from neighbouring skys risers. The streets are no longer filled with traffic coming from each and every way, but with streets made out of cobblestones, trees and benches. All of the streets and parking lots have been rebuilt underground to make more room for businesses and a cleaner environment. We borrowed this idea that was used in Boston in 1999. The city of Boston put all of their major expressways underground, it actually was a very useful idea. The city is cleaner and seems to attract more tourists. Soon this idea will be put to use in northern parts of the province. They started the trend in Toronto in 2008 and it quickly spread to the other larger cities across Canada by 2010. The underground expressways

282

were bringing people to their destinations much more quickly, but in 2007 the C.R.R. (Canadian Rail Road) released their new trains. These trains could travel eight times faster than the old models used in the 1990s.

I look out the window of the 11:45 p.m. train that will bring me to the west end of town, where I live. I sit in my lounging chair with my feet reclined and I can't help but think of how much the ways of living have changed. The world's population has increased by almost two billion over the last two years and everybody has eternal youth and health on their minds. It's quite overwhelming at times, for the majority of people are looking at medicine to improve their lifestyles, not themselves. It's a pity, really, because although we are able to postpone our death by at least twenty years, it is now a matter of finding a way to get people to live happily for an extra twenty years or so.

Five minutes later I arrive at my stop and I am finally home. Home to me and to many other people is a loft in the outskirts of the old suburban parts of town. Actual houses are too expensive, and with an increase in apartments over the last five years, rent has gone down dramatically. My one and only child is in bed and my husband of thirteen years is in bed, with the television on, of course, even though he knows it's not good for his sleeping patterns. Like most people we decided that we only want to have one child. Education costs us thousands of dollars a year and post-secondary education costs approximately 8,000 dollars to 14,000 dollars a year, and that's only for college; university costs anywhere from 15,000 dollars to 35,000 dollars a year. It's not only education that costs a ton of money, the general cost of living has skyrocketed over the last ten years or so. I crawl into bed and I hear the news reporter talking about a new, unknown disease that has claimed another 45 lives over the last week in southern Ontario. I turn the television off, kiss my husband goodnight and try to imagine what the world will be like when my daughter is my age.

283

Grade OAC
Northeastern Catholic
District School Board

Melissa M. Maltais

Le bateau Freedom

Les édifices sont si grands
qu'ils touchent les nuages.

Aujourd'hui les astronautes
vont à Jupiter. «NASA» est en
charge de cette mission.

Le bateau «Freedom»
va autour du monde toutes
les deux années.

Mais, même s'il y a beaucoup
de voitures, il ne font pas de
pollution parce qu'ils sont
électriques. On les recharge
chaque deux années.

Les avions comme ceux
d'Air Canada ont six moteurs
à réaction et vont à 10,000 km
par heure!

Mais si tu penses que ça c'est
difficile à croire, ceci va te
choquer. Les barres de chocolat
coûtent 20 $ chacune!

Les voitures sont si rapides!
Sais-tu comment vite?
Les voitures vont aussi vite
que les avions de nos jours.

Andrew Brown

3e année / Grade 3
Conseil scolaire du district des écoles
catholiques de Sud-Ouest de l'Ontario

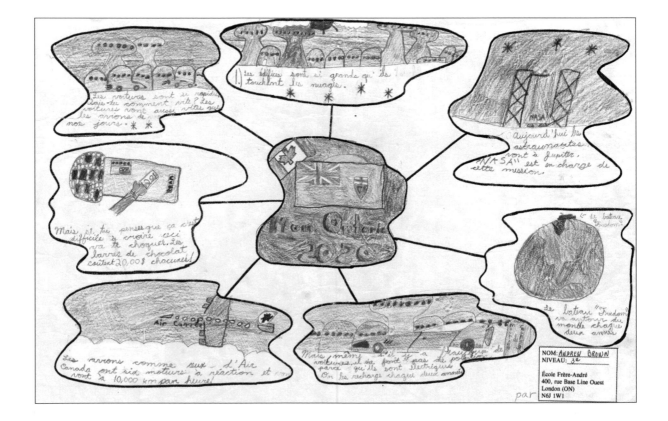

What I Think the World Will Be Like in the Year 2020

What do I think the world will be like in the year 2020? Hmm, well let me introduce myself. My name is Jen and I think Ontario is a really great place to live in, I mean, no wars, not very much crime, and wonderful people! In 2020, Ontario will still have great people and will still be a great place to live in, but people will probably be driving around in something really neat like space mobiles that don't need gas, they will run on water or a fuel that won't hurt the environment, but they will be able to go really, really fast. We could have robots that will do all our chores and housework for us, make supper, take the robo dog for a walk, you know, the boring things.

Pardon, what did you say? Oh, what do I think the food will be like? Maybe, when we are sleeping, we could hook ourselves up to a tube and it would pump in all the food we need to eat for a day, so we wouldn't have to taste it or take the time to eat. Or we could take a pill that has all the vitamins in it that we need for one meal, then we would take another one that has water in it or juice. Hopefully we will still eat ice cream out of the container the old-fashioned way.

Do I think that the world will still have racism and wars and will people get hurt? Well, that's up to the people. I don't know when they are going to realize that everybody is equal and it doesn't matter what colour your skin is: light or dark; what your language is: English, French, German, Chinese we're all the same on the inside and that's all that counts. And wars, I don't see why people won't sign peace treaties, there is lots of land for people to share, people are very greedy.

We can all help keep the earth beautiful if we try together, try walking or riding your bike instead of driving a car, car pool instead of driving by yourself, take a bus, turn off the water when you are brushing your teeth, pick up a piece of trash in the park or on the side of the road. It will make a difference if we all work together, but if only one person tries then it will keep getting worse.

I will try to make a difference in our world by helping people when they need help, trying to stop racism, maybe even running for mayor and trying to help my communities by having races to raise money to fix up our town or build a park for all the children, or annual cleanup days to help keep our town clean. I think living in Ontario in the year 2020 will be really fun, we will advance in technology, hopefully cut down on pollution, and make the world a better place to live in!

285

Grade 6 / 6e année
Hamilton-Wentworth
District School Board

Jennifer Hart

Millennium Bears

My name is Healthy Food Bear. I care about food. My job is to remind people to eat healthy food, so that in 2020 people are healthy.

My name is Animal Bear. I care about the earth. My job is to remind people not to kill the animals, so that in 2020 we have animals on our planet.

My name is Friendship Bear. I care about the world and sharing too, so that in 2020 the people will share.

My name is Hospital Bear. I care about people if they get hurt. I would help them, so that in 2020 there will be healthier people.

My name is Flower Bear. I care about flowers. My job is to remind people to plant flowers, so that in 2020 the world is pretty.

My name is Tree Bear. I care about trees.

My name is Love Bear. I care about the world. My job is to remind people to love each other, so that in 2020 there will be no wars. That is my job!

My name is Peace Bear. My job is to remind people to be kind to each other, so that in 2020 there is no war, and people are nice to everyone too.

My name is Water Bear. I tell people not to pollute, so we can have clean water in 2020, so we can enjoy looking at the sea creatures.

My name is Teacher Bear. I care about the world. My job is to remind teachers to keep teaching the kids, so that in 2020 the grownups can help the teachers keep the world clean and go to church.

My name is Forest Bear. I care about the trees so they don't get cut down, because then the birds won't have a home in 2020.

My name is Medicine Bear. I love people. My job is to keep animals alive.

My name is Sea Creature Bear. My job is to keep the sea creatures alive.

My name is Recycling Bear. I tell people to put their garbage in the recycling, so the world in 2020 will be clean.

My name is Big Bird Bear. I care about the world. My job is not to shoot the birds down out of the sky, so that in 2020 they are still flying in the air.

My name is Energy Bear. I care about energy. My job is to remind people to keep energy, so that in 2020 there will be energy left over.

My name is Explorer Bear. I take care of the mountains to make sure the mountains are clean, so in 2020 people can go skiing.

My name is Space Bear. I go to different planets. I can teach people to go up in space in 2020.

My name is Clean-Up Bear. I care about the world by keeping the parks clean.

My name is Christian Bear. I would tell people to go to church, so that in 2020 people would get holy.

My name is Farmer Bear. I care about the world. My job is to remind farmers to get meat from pigs, so that in 2020 we have food.

My name is Food Bear. I care about food. My job is to remind people to plant lots of vegetables, so that in 2020 we still have lots of food.

Andre
Angela
Brandon
Briana
Brittni
Corson
Eric
James
Joey
Jessica
Kevin
Kirsten
Krysta
Kyle
Melanie
Melissa
Rachel
Randall
Richard
Sebastian
Stephanie
Tyler

Grade 1 / 1re année

287

288

My "2020" Vision for Ontario

As the new millennium quickly approaches, I can only imagine the changes this will bring. Most people are concerned about the computer problems that may arise on January 1, 2000, at 12:00 a.m., but has anyone thought about the year 2020? With all the changes occurring every day, the possibilities for the future seem endless. I envision that the social, health, and environmental issues will undergo the greatest changes in Ontario by the year 2020.

My vision of the year 2020 is quite positive. I like to believe the best in people and I see the residents of Ontario working together to shape a great future. By the year 2020, I imagine that Ontario will be the Canadian province to have the least amount of homelessness. I would not hesitate to help someone less fortunate. I hope to contribute by being involved with a foundation to raise money in many forms. With the money, a group of people could work together to build more shelters and homes for homeless families. I realize that there are people who dislike accepting charity, but an agreement could be made so that the family could pay back the money in small portions whenever possible. With this agreement, the less fortunate will not feel too obliged.

I hope another social reform will involve adolescents. Right now, there are many young adults with personal problems who are not receiving help. These problems may include school, friends, family, addictions, and crimes. Community-based activities in the future will be valuable assets solving many of these conflicts. Since I am a teenager, I can relate to some of these adolescent issues. I want to help solve these problems by becoming involved with teen hotlines and listening to people's troubles. Presently, I can assist by listening to my friends' difficulties and offering my advice and opinions if they want them. These are a few of the social issues that I am encouraged to participate in and support in the future.

Throughout this century, there have been many medical advances that have greatly improved the quality of life for people. In the past, cures for many fatal diseases have been discovered. During the new millennium, more treatments and cures may be revealed. My interest in the medical field may lead me to aid in treatments for diseases such as cancer or AIDS. Currently, I am contributing to health care by donating money and participating in community events that support worthwhile medical issues. Health care has always been a major government concern. The public often advocates better health care and as a result, Ontario may become one of the most advanced provinces regarding medical issues in the year 2020.

An unpolluted natural environment has always been every community's goal. Over the years, humans have often interacted with and modified their surroundings to suit their needs. Although these changes and interactions may benefit humans, they may be detrimental to the environment. Individuals have become aware of many factors that affect our ecosystem in a negative manner, but have also recognized the importance of equilibrium. With these new realizations, people are now involved in environmentally conscious activities. If these activities continue to increase, by the year 2020 Ontario may be extremely sophisticated with environmentally friendly products. I imagine that one of the projects that will significantly aid the environment is the monorail. The monorail will run by solar power during the day and by battery during the night. It will also be a quicker form of transportation than cars or trains and much more convenient since it does not deal with road traffic. Currently, I am doing my part by recycling, reducing, reusing, and composting. This may not seem like much, but every little bit can add up and help. Since another of my interests involves teaching, I would teach the younger generation the importance of a healthy environment. Environmental issues of the future can alter lives rapidly even though they may be different from the ones we are dealing with today.

It is difficult to envision the future for Ontario since changes are occurring at a rapid pace even before we enter the new millennium. Even though I believe the social, health, and environmental issues will undergo the greatest changes, there are still many other aspects that can affect Ontario's society tremendously. Over the next twenty years, I hope to contribute to the improvements in these areas as well as many more, however small my contributions may seem. I have learned that sometimes a little can mean a great deal. Despite all the improvements that the year 2020 may bring, problems may still plague individuals. An example of this is as technology gets more advanced, people become too dependent on it. A carefully planned future can result in a "2020" vision for Ontario.

Grade 10 / 10e année
District School Board of Niagara

Emily Yee

Dans l'an 2020

Il y aura des animaux qui manqueront de nourriture à cause de leur reproduction trop rapide. Et il y aura moins de forêts.

290

Ottawa sera immense.

Et peut-être que Hull fera partie de l'Ontario.

Il y aura peut-être quatre climats: tempéré, continental, subpolaire et polaire...

et cinq forêts: arbres à feuilles caduques, taïga, boréale, mixte et extramixte.

Les champs des cultivateurs seront remplis de maisons.

291

Dans le monde entier, l'ordinateur sera peut-être l'objet le plus célèbre.

Il y aura plus de villes.

Des robots avec des commandes.

292

Et plus de chaînes de télévision.

Tout cela en Ontario dans l'an 2020!

4e année / Grade 4
Conseil scolaire du district catholique
de l'Est Ontarien

Mathieu-Philippe Perras

Short but Insightful Perspectives

I think that in the year 2020, we will be living in outer space. Some people will live on the moon, some people will be living on Mars. There will be flying cars and other cool things.

I think Ontario will be different than it is now. The cars will be different and even the houses. We might have robots to do stuff for us. The province can even become bigger.

In 2020 crime will be up. But if I am Prime Minister I will increase money to schools and other non-profit organizations.

In 2020 I will be 32 years old. I'm not too sure what it is going to be like because it depends on what our technology is like. I can contribute to this by using the high tech equipment.

In the year 2020 I think there will be more crime. I will teach my children to take care of the world like not to litter.

In the year 2020 I think this world will be one giant garbage can unless we figure out how to take care of it. I also think technology will be really advanced, probably so only highly educated people could use it, which hopefully will encourage people to do better in school.

I think that Ontario will be the same except for more technology, "no floating cars," more pollution and less jobs.
I want to help this because I want to invent stuff.

I'm not sure that Ontario will be that different from now. Unless it's the start of a "technology state" or "spurt." In which case, everything as we know it today will be very old fashioned in the year 2020. I think that if I do anything important, I may visit classrooms to talk to students and give money for conservation and use my influence. But if I don't do anything important, I think that I'll still try to do my best to help the world.

Matthew Berube
Amanda Colles
Dayna Hudson
Jacqueline Stitson
Shawn Taylor

Grade 7 / 7ᵉ année

Ashley
Jonathan Bin
Jessie Sauder

Grade 8 / 8ᵉ année

294

My Keep Safe Community

I would like Ontario to have cleaner air. To make that possible,
I think people should travel in car pools, subways, bicycles and
buses rather than their own cars. Spray bottles that interfere with
the ozone layer would be taken off the market. I would like kids
to get together and plant more trees.

I would help make neighborhoods safe by being part of a
community foundation that I would call, (and be the president of)
Keep Safe. I would build the houses sponsored by our program
in a circle so that parents could keep an eye on their children in
the center playground. The communities that I build will be
wheelchair accessible as well.

My picture shows my Keep Safe Community.

Grade 4 / 4ᵉ année
Simcoe County District School Board

Bailey

Dreams to Reality

Ontario, my Ontario, I see you there
In two thousand twenty
As a pearl in the ocean mighty,
On earth a precious lustrous spot.

For a pearl to attain this height of beauty,
Removed it should be from its shell, where hides its bounty,
Washed, polished, and then will its lustre be shown.
And to do just that, to make it shine
Here we are; you and me.

Come let us all unite, make our differences our strength,
Let the Canadian mosaic endure another test,
Work to achieve a lustre beyond compare and be the best.
Let the maple put the diamonds and the stars to shame,
Let the world, in praise, chant our name,
Make Canada proud of its treasure,
Work towards prosperity, joy, and pleasure.

I know it is possible; I know it can happen,
As I dare to dream, with you beside me
Dreams can surely turn into reality.

Waiz Ahmed

Grade OAC / OAC année
Toronto District School Board

Une question pour le futur

8e année / Grade 8
Toronto Catholic District School Board

Ly Nguyen

297

My Ontario 2020

In the year 2020 I will be thirty years old. I might be looking for a nice home. Maybe I will be looking at good educated schools for my children. I will be looking for a car that will run a different way that is not bad for the environment. Maybe I will be the next woman Prime Minister.

Now and to the year 2020, I really hope that there will be cures for AIDS, CANCER, and other medical sickness. I also hope there will be homes for the homeless people so they can have a home that is safe, clean and where no one can bug them or make fun of them.

I hope computer technology will keep on getting larger and larger. I am looking forward to a new selection off of the computer that is sort of like the Internet. I think there might be a machine that is controlled by a computer.

The year 2020 will be a new millennium. Also, it will be the twenty-first century. I hope there will be more interesting things in the year 2020. My Ontario is a great province to live in but I will really have to wait until the year 2020 to really know what is happening.

298

Hollie Matthews

Grade 5 / 5e année
Peel District School Board

My Ideas about the Future

This is what I think Ontario will be like. It will be great or gloomy but who knows. I think it will be just the same. Different people, well, they might get funnier, or weirder, but I sure hope it will not get wrong. Less schools might be bad. Different creatures might be good or bad. Less violence would be grrrrrreat! Less companies will be bad. Doughnuts might change. Disney will be excellent and get more characters and then they might be world famous and people will love them.

Another CN Tower would be excellent but way much better. New schools would be good. Two more Titanics would be way much better and both of them will be unsinkable. These are my ideas about the future of Ontario....I will like it. I hope that I won't die in the future like in the 21st century. I hope that you will not die either because you're the bestest teacher ever! New soccer teams will be good and new hockey teams like a Hampton Team or ExtraHuge Team or there might even have other greater teams.

Grade 5 / 5ᵉ année
Peel District School Board

Trevor Stewart

Ma vision de l'an 2020

Je vais bientôt avoir 33 ans… Que de choses se sont passées depuis la fin de mes études. J'habite maintenant à Métropolis, la nouvelle cité lacustre installée au sud de Toronto, sur le lac Ontario. Métropolis fut construite il y a tout juste cinq ans. Ces architectes l'ont conçue comme la réflexion artistique et créative de notre vieille cité. Toronto a gardé sa vocation de «lieu de rencontres» puisque le siège de La Paix internationale s'y trouve. Métropolis est composée d'une grande communauté artistique, de peintres, musiciens, écrivains, etc.

J'y enseigne les arts plastiques et visuels. Je vais souvent rendre visite à ma famille en France. Les voyages inter-continentaux sont tellement plus agréables depuis la création de la navette orbitale : Toronto-Paris se fait maintenant en une heure et demie. Mais revenons un peu en arrière…

Bien sûr, le monde a connu sa panique apocalyptique au 1er janvier de l'an 2000. J'avais 13 ans à l'époque et je me rappelle encore célébrer l'ère nouvelle avec les feux d'artifice de Victoria Park. Et puis Y2K? Beaucoup de bruit pour pas grand-chose. On a eu un super «Black-Out», des yaourts avec des drôles de dates d'expiration mais pas plus.

Quand je suis allée à l'université, nous avons failli perdre mon chat adoré «Ace» qui commençait à se faire bien vieux, mais grâce au développement des techniques de clonage, j'ai pu retrouver un jeune Ace qui ressemble tout à fait au chat de mon enfance.

J'ai rencontré l'homme de ma vie en 2010 lors du voyage inaugural de la navette orbitale (j'avais gagné ce prix dans un concours car à cette époque le coût d'un tel voyage était phénoménal!). Gabriel venait d'Australie pour assister à un festival interculturel en Chine. J'ai débarqué avec lui à Pékin et j'ai assisté à la naissance de l'unisson de toutes les nations. Depuis quelques années, il y avait un fort courant chez les jeunes qui désiraient un changement dans l'ordre politique du monde.

Nous voulions un monde plus juste, paisible, sans faim. On était très proche d'un désastre nucléaire mondial. Maintenant toute arme nucléaire est interdite et s'il y a encore des conflits entre pays, ces pays sont exclus des échanges jusqu'à ce qu'ils résolvent leurs problèmes, un peu comme le «time-out» de mon enfance.

J'ai deux jumelles, Arielle et Cléo, qui ont sept ans et qui vont à une école bien différente de la mienne : c'est une école internationale où elles apprennent trois langues au minimum. Elles n'y vont que trois jours par semaine car une bonne partie de l'apprentissage se fait à l'extérieur comme par exemple à la Cité des Sciences. Le travail papier-crayon a presque complètement disparu et elles travaillent déjà beaucoup plus à l'ordinateur.

À la maison, elles aiment jouer avec Ace III, et nous passons beaucoup de temps ensemble car le système informatique s'occupe d'organiser les tâches, la vaisselle, la lessive, l'épicerie commandée directement, le maintien du véhicule, etc. Nous ne sommes pas exactement habillés comme les «Jetsons» mais nos vêtements sont dessinés directement à l'ordinateur à notre goût, ce qui nous offre bien plus de variété et de créativité. Nous avons encore des centres d'achats pour ceux qui aiment faire leurs emplettes à l'ancienne mais c'est tellement démodé!

Nous sommes encore à la recherche de vie extra-terrestre et attendons le retour d'une équipe d'exploration d'une nouvelle planète qui vient juste d'apparaître dans notre vieux système solaire. Nous avons aussi une colonie de pionniers sur la Lune mais je crois qu'ils s'y embêtent beaucoup car il n'y a pas grand-chose à faire et les conditions de séjour ne sont pas encore très confortables. Peut-être, quand ils auront fini l'aménagement de la station de vacances lunaires, j'irai y faire un tour avec Gabriel. Pour voir un clair de Terre.

301

7e année / Grade 7
Conseil scolaire du district
du Centre-Sud-Ouest

Gaïa Orain-Wark

Robot Super Génie

L'an 2020 arrive à grands pas. Notre Ontario prévoit de gros changements qui vont tout changer.

Mon Ontario en 2020 sera le paradis. Imaginez-vous, l'école sera à la maison dans ton salon. Ton prof sera un R.S.G., un Robot Super Génie. Tout se fera par ordinateur. Même quand tu voudras téléphoner à quelqu'un, tu composeras le numéro de téléphone sur les chiffres du clavier et quand la personne va répondre tu la verras sur ton écran. Génial, non?

Les sports

Les sports seront sophistiqués, très spécial si vous voulez. Les Jeux olympiques se passeront dans l'espace. Les skieurs partiront dans une fusée pour l'espace et celui qui arrivera le premier sur terre, en ski, gagnera. Pour le biathlon, ce sera encore sur terre jusqu'en 2030.

Pour que cela se réalise, il faudra que j'en parle à de grands scientifiques. Pour les sports, je devrai le réaliser moi-même avec des ami(e)s et plusieurs autres personnes. J'adorerai mon Ontario comme il sera!

Une passionnée de l'Ontario

302

Marie-Ève

6ᵉ année / Grade 6
Conseil scolaire du district catholique
des Grandes Rivières

Un beau rêve

Ha! J'ai fait un beau rêve! Maman, Maman, écoute, j'ai rêvé…
qu'une soucoupe volante est arrivée à l'école et c'est moi qui suis
allée dedans. Je suis rentrée dans la soucoupe et je suis allée voir
l'Ontario de l'an 2020, c'était tellement beau!

Plus de pollution! Les gens font tellement attention! À chaque
fois qu'un déchet est par terre les gens le ramassent. Je trouvais ça
extraordinaire! De plus il y a beaucoup moins d'autos! Maintenant
les gens prennent leurs bicyclettes ou bien ils marchent. Parfois ils
prennent leur auto pour aller à l'extérieur de la ville. Maman,
je me sentais si bien dans cette belle ville.

Et puis, c'est pas tout! Plus de violence, tout le monde s'aime,
c'est tellement beau et bon de les voir. On se dit "Bonjour,
comment vas-tu?" C'était SUPER!

Mon rêve se termine ainsi! Il était beau, mon rêve, tu ne trouves
pas? Et je connais un moyen de réaliser ce rêve. Je commence tout
de suite! Plus de chicanes! Plus de déchets. Je pars à l'instant pour
ramasser les déchets de notre cour!

Moi, je veux que l'Ontario soit beau et propre!

303

5e année / Grade 5
Conseil scolaire du district catholique
de l'Est Ontarien

Maxyme Denis

My School in 2020

SCHOOL

In the year 2020
I would like
students to
be able to
come into all
schools who are
in wheelchairs.

By: April 9 1999   Date: RICARDO Serrano

Ricardo Serrano

Grade 1 / 1re année
Peel District School Board

I Can Make It Happen

My Ontario 2020
is technology,
with advanced computers
and houses run by them.

My Ontario 2020
is cars run by another resource,
water not gas.

My Ontario 2020
is school at home,
better education preparing you
for better jobs.

My Ontario 2020
is less violence
on television and in Ontario.

My Ontario 2020
is homes for everyone,
no one on the streets
and no one in shelters.

My Ontario 2020
is a better environment
with no pollution in it.

My Ontario 2020
is better health care,
cures for diseases,
and help for everyone.

My Ontario 2020
is nicer people,
who help everyone.

I can make this
all happen by
finishing school.
Education is important.

Kristie Gillespie

Grade 8 / 8e année
Thames Valley District School Board

305

Year 2020: It Will Be Fun

In the year 2020 I think the world will be a different place.
We'll probably be able to travel from planet to planet.
Maybe scientists will find life on Mars.
I think humans will live on other planets.
Wonderland will be out of this world.
Everyone will own a rocketship.
People will wear skintight clothes and rings around their outfits.
Dogs will be a special species and cats will be extinct.
Scarce animals will be repopulated.
Homes will be like castles and everyone will have the same amount of money.
Sidewalks will move.
Tigers will be pets and other animals too.
Everyone will be equal and everyone will be fair.
It will be fun.
There will be no such thing as pollution.
There will be no such thing as Endangered species of Ontario. I will help by giving the sick and weak animals nutrition and help and stop hunters from shooting them.
Hopefully we will be able to help make it happen so the world and Ontario could be a better place.

306

Allison Petts

Grade 5 / 5ᵉ année
York Region District School Board

If You Wanna Have a Good Life

(The chorus is sung to the tune of "Wannabe" by Spice Girls, the rest of the song is a rap.)

Chorus:
If you wanna have a good life
You have got to see
Polluting may be easy
But it isn't good for me.

If you wanna have a good life
Please listen to my plea
Don't litter anymore
And what a better world it will be.

Verse #1:
Now let me tell you about what I know
About a fabulous place called Ontario
Once upon a time it was a good place to go
Because there were very few cars
And many more stars
There was also no smog
Just a little bit of fog.

Chorus:
If you wanna have a good life
You have got to see
Polluting may be easy
But it isn't good for me.

Verse #2:
Ontario today isn't what it once was
The answer here is simply because
There are fewer trees
And a harmful breeze
Our garbage dumps are overfilled
So if you don't recycle you should be billed
Our health and safety are at risk
If our O-Zone layer keeps going amiss
Ontario's vast lands are being filled
By construction companies who don't care where
they build.

Chorus.
If you wanna have a good life
You have got to see
Polluting may be easy
But it isn't good for me.

If you wanna have a good life
Please listen to my plea
Don't litter anymore
And what a better world it will be.

Verse #3:
In the year 2020 I want Ontario to be
A place without racism about nationality
Also a place with freedom to roam
Wherever you wish and you won't be alone
In the year 2020 I wish I could see
Clear skies full of stars and a sun that
won't harm me
World peace and no war would be a success
If only we could resolve the present political mess
In the year 2020 I hope Ontario will be
A cleaner environment for both you and me.

Chorus:
If you wanna have a good life
You have got to see
Polluting may be easy
But it isn't good for me.

If you wanna have a good life
Please listen to my plea
Don't litter anymore
And what a better world it will be.

307

Grade 5 / 5e année
Toronto Catholic District School Board

Lauren Miele

My Invention for 2020

308

The problem I want to solve for the year 2020 is drinking and driving. If you drink and drive you have a good chance of being hurt or even killed. In every car there should be a breath tester the can tell if you were drinking. If you take the test and you fail then the car wouldn't start. If you weren't drinking and you take the test and pass then the car would start up. After you take the breath test it will tell you to start up the car if you passed the test, to wait a while if you just barely failed, or to try again later if you completely failed. I think this is a good idea because it would eliminate drinking and driving, and it could save lives.

Jillian Renaud

Grade 6 / 6ᵉ année
Bruce-Grey Catholic
District School Board

Houses of the Year 2020

My Ontario

Ashley Quinn
Grade 6/7
Balaclava
Public
School

Houses From Year 2020

The houses from year 2020 are automatic. For example, instead of turning on taps, ovens, showers, lights and the list keeps on going on. Just clap once or twice whatever it's programed to and it will turn on. The rings around it are for the cars that go all the way up into the garage. If you don't want to go the whole way up you will find elevator doors on every floor. When you get in, there is a whole selection of elevators and escalators.

Grade 6 / 6e année
Hamilton-Wentworth
District School Board

Ashley Quinn

My Purpose

These are my visions of Ontario in the year 2020. Now, I know that they're totally unrealistic, but these are my dreams, so bear with me.

All people would be kind, caring, and sincere. Crime would not exist, people would not lie, steal, cheat, or kill. Rape and abuse would only be a distant memory, reminding us all to do our part to stop it in other countries and parts of the world.

People would do things out of the goodness and kindness of their hearts and not because they expected something in return.

There would be no such thing as cruelty towards people, animals, our environment, or anything else. People would live safely and happily, not in fear and uneasiness. People would feel safe wherever they go and be confident in whatever they do.

Starvation and homelessness would never be an issue because all people, and I mean absolutely everybody, all over Ontario, would have jobs and each individual would earn the same income, money would be distributed equally among all people. Not one person would earn or have more than another.

We will find a way to clean up the environment and everything: cars, buses, planes, factories, everything would be "user friendly" and environmentally safe.

Technology will be and will have been booming and great developments will have been made. Cures for diseases will have been found and put to use, and those not already discovered will be under research and soon developed. New diseases would never disappear and people would be healthy and prospering.

Now, I know that all this is absolutely impossible, but throughout my life I will work and strive towards making Ontario as close to this dream as possible. I'll support and involve myself in as many contributing groups as I can and maybe even start one or some of my own. I'll stand up for what I believe in and never falter from my purpose.

Emily Going

Grade 3 / 3ᵉ année
Simcoe County District School Board

My Neighbourhood — Toronto 2020

This is what I think my neighbourhood will look like in the year 2020.
It is made of clay and it is very delicate.

311

Grade 2 / 2ᵉ année
Toronto District School Board

Chelsea

If We All Work Together

In the year 2020, I would like to see,
the forests we have today and a smart,
famous me.
If we could invent a cure for each and every disease that has taken so many lives,
If we could burn all the weapons, all the guns, bombs and knives,
If we could clean the water and unpollute the air,
And if brothers and sisters would stop fighting and share,
If we would recycle more, instead of throwing things away,
Then the sun would shine through, almost every day.
If we would encourage more, to stop smoking and that drugs are very bad,
We will have the best Ontario that we have ever had.
If we all work together, and set out on my quest,
I'm promising you, our province will be the best.

Linzi Leclerc

Grade 5 / 5ᵉ année
Upper Canada District School Board

312

My Ontario Will Be Fun

In 2020 we are going to have a lot of fun. Everything will be nice and pretty because we won't litter and we will keep Ontario nice and clean. We are going to make more schools so everyone can learn. We will have lots of libraries with lots of fun books in print and in braille.

Grade 1 / 1re année
Ottawa-Carleton Catholic School Board

Nolan Jenikov

314

Names appear as requested by the student, parent or guardian.

Les noms apparaissent tels que demandés par l'élève, la parent ou le tuteur ou la tutrice.

316

317

319

320

To the students whose faces are on the cover of *My Ontario*, thanks for participating in the photograph sessions and appearing as cover "models."

Nous remercions les élèves dont le visage apparaît sur la couverture de Mon Ontario *d'avoir participé aux séances de photo et de figurer comme «mannequins» de la page couverture.*

ALGOMA DISTRICT SCHOOL BOARD
Elliot, Alan
Gilles, W.
Hipetti, Allison
Rosso, Ms. Mary
Seccariccia, Ms. Nicole

AVON MAITLAND DISTRICT SCHOOL BOARD
Griffin, Waverley
Hearn, Sherrie
Roch, Gladys, Principal

BLUEWATER DISTRICT SCHOOL BOARD
Eadie, A. Anne

BRANDT-HALDIMAND-NORFOLK CATHOLIC DISTRICT
SCHOOL BOARD
Hinton, Sandy

BRUCE-GREY CATHOLIC DISTRICT SCHOOL BOARD
Bushey, Mike
Legace, Robert

CATHOLIC DISTRICT SCHOOL BOARD OF EASTERN
ONTARIO
Boyd, Marlene
Chaplin, Lori
Stuart, Tony

CHRISTIAN ISLAND ELEMENTARY SCHOOL
Armstrong, Alex

CONSEIL DES ÉCOLES PUBLIQUES DE L'EST DE L'ONTARIO
Chartrand, Joyce
Lefebvre, Michelle

CONSEIL SCOLAIRE DU DISTRICT CATHOLIQUE
DE L'EST ONTARIEN
Bergevin, Suzanne
Boulerice, Benoit
Gauthier Normand
Malboeuf, Jacinte

CONSEIL SCOLAIRE DU DISTRICT CATHOLIQUE CENTRE-SUD
McLean, Joël M.

CONSEIL SCOLAIRE DU DISTRICT CATHOLIQUE DES
GRANDES RIVIÈRES
Fortier-Levesque, Nicole

CONSEIL SCOLAIRE DU DISTRICT CATHOLIQUE DU
CENTRE-EST DE L'ONTARIO
Cote, Huguette

CONSEIL SCOLAIRE DU DISTRICT DES ÉCOLES
CATHOLIQUES DE SUD-OUEST DE L'ONTARIO
Chartrand, Luc
Crawford, Madame Isabel
Kelly-Renaud, Marilyn
Legault, Patricia
Vido, Mme. Marie

CONSEIL SCOLAIRE DU DISTRICT DU CENTRE-SUD-OUEST
Dahary, Celine
Gagnon, Martine
Glass, Jeremy (Simon)

CONSEIL SCOLAIRE DU DISTRICT DU NORD-EST
DE L'ONTARIO
Houle, Roger
Paiement Shipway, Ginette

CONSEIL SCOLAIRE DE GOGAMA
Poulin, Jennifer-Lynn

CONSEIL SCOLAIRE DU DISTRICT DU GRAND NORD
DE L'ONTARIO
LaForte, Francine
Robouin-Coursol, Sylvie

DISTRICT SCHOOL BOARD OF NIAGARA
Marchese, Rosita
Toews-Peplinski, Allison

DISTRICT SCHOOL BOARD ONTARIO NORTH EAST
Boisvert, Mrs. B.
Thompson, R.

DUFFERIN-PEEL CATHOLIC DISTRICT SCHOOL BOARD
Calderone, H.
Chianelli, Miss P.
Clark, C.
Desbottes, G.
Devlin, Ms. C., Principal
Dillon, Jean A.
Evans, Mrs. H.
Gallant, Kimberly
Jusys, Mrs. R.
Longstreet, L.
Martin, Julie
Romanchych, L.

DURHAM CATHOLIC DISTRICT SCHOOL BOARD
Consoli, Mr. Frank
Gazeley, Mrs. Tiffany
Hague, Mrs. Patricia
Smith, Mrs. Christine

DURHAM DISTRICT SCHOOL BOARD
Wason, Karen

HALTON CATHOLIC DISTRICT SCHOOL BOARD
Kuchma, Ms. J.
Pasceri, M.

HALTON DISTRICT SCHOOL BOARD
Frees, Fay
Ross, J.

HAMILTON-WENTWORTH DISTRICT SCHOOL BOARD
Ellis, Robert
German, Linda
Lees, Judy
MacLaren, Miss Patricia
Picotti, Ranieri

HASTINGS AND PRINCE EDWARD DISTRICT SCHOOL BOARD
Elliot, Mrs. W.
Hay, Sharon
Rodine, Mrs. N.

KEEWATIN-PATRICIA DISTRICT SCHOOL BOARD
Fossey, S. J.

LAKEHEAD DISTRICT SCHOOL BOARD
Corbett, Kathryn
Riva, Nicole
Schutte, Jill

LAMBTON KENT DISTRICT SCHOOL BOARD
Welton, Mr. David

LIMESTONE DISTRICT SCHOOL BOARD
Kingsbury, Dawn

LONDON DISTRICT CATHOLIC SCHOOL BOARD
Reid, Carmen
Thielk, Ann Marie

NIAGARA CATHOLIC DISTRICT SCHOOL BOARD
LePera, Jonathan

NORTHEASTERN CATHOLIC DISTRICT SCHOOL BOARD
Clausi, Louis

NORTHWEST CATHOLIC DISTRICT SCHOOL BOARD
Martin, Ms. Lynn

OTTAWA-CARLETON CATHOLIC SCHOOL BOARD
Aprile, Pina
Delage, Ann
Garth, P.
Peddie, David
Salole, Becky

OTTAWA-CARLETON DISTRICT SCHOOL BOARD
Lambert, Mme. L.
McCormick, Mrs. G.

PEEL DISTRICT SCHOOL BOARD
Adlam, Mark
Argue, Barbara
Baker, Mrs. Elaine
Christensen, Julie
De Angelis, Stephanie
Emerson, Mrs. Heather
Innes, Mrs. Sandy
Katsogianopoulos, Soula
Laughlin, Rosina
Lehman, Virginia
Lewis, Mrs. Ruth
Mackintosh, Mrs. Jane
McVean, Miss Caitlin
Richardson, Sharon
Thomas, David K.
White, Diane
Young, Julie

PETERBOROUGH VICTORIA NORTHUMBERLAND AND CLARINGTON CATHOLIC DISTRICT SCHOOL BOARD
Fowler, Michelle
Stewart, Marion

RED LAKE AREA AND COMBINED ROMAN CATHOLIC SEPARATE SCHOOL BOARD
Martel, Marlene

RENFREW COUNTY DISTRICT SCHOOL BOARD
Moffat, Mr. Ron

SIMCOE COUNTY DISTRICT SCHOOL BOARD
Lee, Judy
Morrison, Mrs. M
Popowich, Mrs. Amy J.

322

SIMCOE MUSKOKA CATHOLIC DISTRICT SCHOOL BOARD
Harvey, Dawn

SUPERIOR NORTH CATHOLIC DISTRICT SCHOOL BOARD
Allaire, Trish
Kutcher, Joseph
LeBlanc, Twila
Radul, Mrs.

THAMES VALLEY DISTRICT SCHOOL BOARD
Armstrong, Lori
Durocher, Julie
Scott, M.

THUNDER BAY CATHOLIC DISTRICT SCHOOL BOARD
Beda, Ms.
Kowalchuk, Mrs. C.

TORONTO CATHOLIC DISTRICT SCHOOL BOARD
Biffis, Jane
Corey, Paul
DiMillo, Mr. Ben
Fiasche, Mrs. D.
Holmes, S.
Listro, Mrs. L.
Nanowska, Anna
Pomorska, Mrs. D.
Sommer, Ms. Sofie
Volk, H.

TORONTO DISTRICT SCHOOL BOARD
Chyczij, Chris
Cresta, Mrs.
Davidson, R.
Dow, Stephen
Dunn, D.
Galati, Grace
Gerriets-Elliot, Mrs.
Girardi, Christina
Halladay, F.
Kean, Matt
Kerrison, Mrs.
Koutsaris, Vasiliki (Bessy)
Legault, Debbie
Lunn, Kelly
Malindrino, Lynne
Marlow, Mary
Marshall, Virginia M.
Pettigrew, Val
Smatlanek, Barbara, Librarian
Stanley, R.
Stickel, Richard
Wason, Karen
Weston, Karen
Wilson, Miss Libby
Wynn, K.

TRILLIUM LAKELANDS DISTRICT SCHOOL BOARD
Marks-O'Sullivan, Mrs. Laurie
Sisson, Mrs. Sue

UPPER CANADA DISTRICT SCHOOL BOARD
Hunter, Jo-Anne
Johnson, Madelyn
Richardson, Mrs.
Robillard, Brent

WATERLOO REGION DISTRICT SCHOOL BOARD
MacMullin, Tammy

WELLINGTON CATHOLIC DISTRICT SCHOOL BOARD
Stafford, Mrs. Theresa

YORK REGION DISTRICT SCHOOL BOARD
Alderson, Lois
Jackson, W.
Leck, Kim
Pridham, Carole
Sanford, Janis
Woods, J.

PRIVATE SCHOOLS:
Rehoboth Christian School, Copetown
Den Boer, Mr. Bill

Trillium Montessori School, Orangeville
Ernst, Nancy

Sommerville Manor Private School, Mississauga
Johnson, W.

Wayside Academy, Peterborough
Sweeney, Ms. Nora

Glebe Montessori School, Ottawa
Sauro, Beverley
Segal, Benna

Guido de Brès Christian High School, Hamilton
Van Dooren, Hans

323

Ontario 2000 would like to thank the following members of the educational community for contributing their guidance, expertise and assistance in the creation of *My Ontario*.

Le programme Ontario 2000 aimerait remercier les membres suivants du milieu de l'enseignement de lui avoir fourni des conseils, de l'expertise et de l'aide quant à la création de Mon Ontario.

Lindy Amato,
Ontario Teachers' Federation
*Fédération des enseignantes et
enseignants de l'Ontario*

Heather Boswell,
Principal, Mono Amaranth Public School, Orangeville
*Directrice, école élémentaire publique
Mono Amaranth, Orangeville*

Clément Bonin,
École secondaire Georges-P.-Vanier, Hamilton
Georges-P.-Vanier Secondary School, Hamilton

Jacqueline Fawcett,
Our Lady of the Valley School, Kenora
École Our Lady of the Valley, Kenora

Preshiel Govind,
Ellesmere-Statton Public School, Scarborough
École élémentaire publique Ellesmere-Statton, Scarborough

Dorothy McAnally,
Streetsville Secondary School, Peel
École secondaire de Streetsville, Peel

Julie Merk,
École Georges Vanier, Elliot Lake
Georges Vanier School, Elliot Lake

Jennifer Mitchell,
The Elementary Teachers' Federation of Ontario
*Fédération des enseignantes et des enseignants
de l'élémentaire de l'Ontario*

Craig Parrott,
Ontario Public School Teachers' Federation
*Fédération des enseignants des écoles
publiques de l'Ontario*

William Reith,
Ontario Secondary School Teachers' Federation
*Fédération des enseignants des écoles
secondaires de l'Ontario*

Judy Reuben,
Emily C. General Elementary School,
Six Nations Reserve, Ohsweken
*École élémentaire publique Emily C. General,
réserve des Six-Nations, Ohsweken*

Theresa Robertson,
Ontario English Catholic Teachers' Association
*Association des enseignants catholiques de langue anglaise
de l'Ontario*

Cathy Warda,
Counselling, Silverthorn Collegiate Institute, Etobicoke
Orientation, Silverthorn Collegiate Institute, Etobicoke

Anne Williamson,
Retired Business Studies Head, York Region
Ancien chef des études commerciales, région de York

All Principals and Teachers who participated in *My Ontario* and helped students become involved in this once-in-a-life-time millennium initiative.

Tous les directeurs et directrices ainsi que tous les enseignants et enseignantes qui ont participé à Mon Ontario *et qui ont aidé les élèves à preudre part à ce projet unique du millénaire.*

324